SAVY

WISDOM

The Parable

By
New York Times Best-Selling Author
Peggy McColl

Hasmark
PUBLISHING
INTERNATIONAL

ISBN 13: 978-1-989756-92-8
ISBN 10: 1989756921

Published by:

Hasmark Publishing International

Important Disclaimers

The author has done their best to present accurate and up-to-date information in this book, but cannot guarantee that the information is correct or will suit your particular situation. Further, the publisher has used its best efforts in preparing this book, and the information provided herein is provided "as is."

We can't guarantee any results from the use of our programs or any of the information contained in this book, though we genuinely believe that this information will help you reach your goals. Like with any program, your results are limited by your willingness to take action as well as factors outside of your control and our control. By reading this book and enrolling in any programs you hereby understand the potential risks when embarking upon a goal achievement journey of any kind and are fully aware and take responsibility for your own results holding Peggy McColl and Dynamic Destinies Inc. harmless.

This is intended for informational purposes only and should not be used as the primary basis for an investment decision. Consult a financial advisor for your personal situation. Please consider the investment objectives, risks, fees, and expenses carefully before investing in anything. Past performance does not guarantee future results.

For more disclaimers that may apply, please view the most up to date information on:

http://www.peggymccoll.com

Cover design by Trace Haskins
Book layout by Trace Haskins

First Edition, 2021

Dedicated

To my family

I love you and cherish you

Endorsements

"Savy wisdom by Peggy McColl made such an impact on my mind - the story - the invaluable personal development lessons that you can apply - and the ending... I was brought to tears and moved in a way I've never been moved by a book before; and you will too!"

~ Anders Hansen

"Savy Wisdom is a compelling and inspiring story with amazing life lessons that leave you with hope, wisdom and light. There's a twist in the story that gave me plenty of goosebumps! It confirmed my belief that you meet people for a reason, like a fortunate stroke of serendipity. I loved it!"

~ L.L. Tremblay
Best-Selling Author of "Seven Roses"

"What I loved most about Savy Wisdom is that when I started reading it, I couldn't put it down. I look forward to adapting this book into a screenplay. It's really great!"

~ Phillip Goldfine
Academy Award Winning Hollywood Producer

"Peggy has done it again! Another book packed with insights and wisdom beyond the norm. I started to read it and couldn't put it down! It was so fascinating I couldn't wait to see what happened next! Thank you Peggy for yet another valuable book!"

~ Jayne Lowell

"Savy Wisdom is the kind of book I love to read. I believe this is your best book yet. I had total goose bumps at the end of the book as well. Great job!"

~ Brian Proctor

"Put Savy Wisdom at the TOP of your must-read list! It's powerful page-turner that takes you on an unforgettable journey. Thank you Peggy!"

~ Selin Bilgin

"Inspiring. Let Savy Wisdom be your guide and light at the end of a tunnel during times of adversity. It was for me and I know it will be for you too."

~ Eric Webb

"Some people love reading for entertainment and to escape their daily life, while others read so that they can learn, grow and go deep within themselves. Savy Wisdom is an amazing story, because it delivers an experience that includes all of the above and more. You will love this book but beware: Once you start reading, you won't want to put it down."

~ Trace Haskins

Table of Contents

Part I

Chapter 1

The park bench I approached seemed to have a shimmering coat of moisture. It was early in the morning as I walked in the neighborhood park. In an effort to sit down, I leaned over and felt the cold and damp wetness on the wood. Even though there were many benches available throughout the park, I chose this one because it was situated at the far corner of the park under a giant willow tree.

I knew this park bench well. I came here with my boyfriend on many occasions, and it was here where we shared our first kiss. We even etched our initials inside a heart into the wood, C for Chad and S for Sophie.

On this morning, I didn't want to be disturbed by anyone or see anyone. With the sleeve of my jacket, I brushed the morning dew away and sat down.

It was Thursday morning around 6:20 a.m. I wasn't normally up this early, but today was different.

The sun was starting to rise, and there was a beautiful red hue cascading across the sky. A thought entered my mind. *Red sky at morning, sailors take warning.*

I wondered, "Is this red sky a warning sign for me?"

The park was void of other people. This was a time when I should have been at home getting ready for school. In an hour, I should be standing at the corner waiting for the school bus to take me to my high school that was located three miles away. I was in the twelfth grade, my final year of high school. But today, I had decided not to go to school. In fact, I had no intention to go back to school ever.

It was a relatively warm morning, and even though the season had recently changed to autumn, it was a comfortable sixty degrees. The leaves on the trees had started to change colors and were beginning to fall. The park was rather large for a small town, with nature trails, an open area for playing games, and a baseball diamond smack in the middle of the park.

On this day, there were plenty of beautiful and colorful leaves on the trees with red, yellow, and orange shades. The evergreen trees mixed in made a spectacular balance adding various shades of green.

In this same park, my hometown of Bridlewood held the annual summer fair called SunFest. During the three-day fair, the park transformed into a magical playground for kids and adults alike, with games, entertainment, and amusement park rides, including Argo excursions. The Argo was an amphibious vehicle with eight wheels, no roof, and would hold up to six passengers at a time. The Argo rides were always my favorite part of the SunFest.

As I sat there on this park bench, allowing memories of my life to flow, I felt an overwhelming sense of sadness. The day before, my high school sweetheart Chad had ended our three-year relationship. As much as it may have felt like a stab in the heart, my intuition had been on high alert, and I knew something wasn't right with the relationship for a month or so.

Chad and I had started dating when I was in grade nine. Even though he wasn't my first choice, he ended up being a wonderful, loving, caring, and attentive boyfriend that I deeply loved.

In my first week of high school, I met Chad's brother Danny in my history class. I remember the day vividly. I was already comfortably seated at a wooden desk in the middle seat of the back row of the class. Our teacher, Mr. Nater, stood at the front, ready to begin. The last of the students poured into the classroom. Danny entered last. I saw him, and it was infatuation at first sight. He had big, round brown eyes, his hair was shiny like silk, and he stood tall and muscular. I found myself sitting there with my mouth gaped open. I started to think I might like high school, after all.

Danny didn't reciprocate with the same feelings, and I could tell he wanted nothing to do with me. Since Danny was on the football team, I decided to try out for the cheerleading squad, and I got in. Danny's older brother Chad also played on the football team. Once I started cheerleading, I went to all of the football games, out of town and home games. I became friendly with many of the players.

Even though I felt this infatuation for Danny, I could tell Danny's brother Chad had an interest in me. He smiled at me. He would intentionally try to sit with me on the bus when going to and from the out-of-town games. He would deliberately spark conversations with me.

After a period of time, with Chad giving me lots of attention, I began to warm up to his attentiveness. It wasn't long before everyone knew Chad and I were dating.

I had never been involved in a serious relationship. And, as much as I was definitely enjoying dating Chad, deep down, I was still pining for Danny. Perhaps there was a hope that dating Chad would get me closer to Danny. But Danny had his eyes on one of my fellow cheerleaders, Becca, and before long, Danny and Becca were an item.

The four of us, Chad and I, Becca and Danny, were going on double dates. It was fun, and my friendship with Becca developed into a close bond. Becca was sweet and innocent. Her parents were medical doctors, and her grandparents on her father's side were surgeons. Becca was pretty, slim, and tall. Her long blond hair flowed all the way down her back to her waist. Even though Becca and I were raised in very different families, and our grades were certainly different (she was a straight-A student, and I was a straight-D student), we really meshed. Our friendship developed into a bond, unlike any other friendship I ever had.

After two months of dating, Chad went on a vacation with his family. His Uncle Jack had moved to another state there years earlier, and they were due for a visit. He was going to be away for an entire week. Chad and I had never been apart for longer than two days. A week apart seemed like an eternity.

Approximately four days after Chad left for the family vacation, I unexpectedly received a letter in the mail. I immediately recognized Chad's handwriting. I never expected to receive a letter from him, so I was pleasantly surprised. With enthusiasm, I grabbed the letter from my mom, raced to my bedroom, sat down on the floor with my back pressed against the door so no one could enter, and began to read.

The letter began with an explanation of some of the fun things they were doing as a family. He wrote about the sites he saw on his travels to his uncle's and the outings he enjoyed with his parents and his two brothers. It was fun to read his letter, as I felt like I was with him. And, then, at the end of the letter, he wrote these three words: *I love you.* No one had ever said that or wrote that to me before. I was shocked. He loved me. Someone loves me. I began to weep like a baby. I didn't realize how much those three words meant to me until that moment. My heart began to swell as I knew I loved him too.

My parents were not very affectionate. Most of the time, the energy in our household was one of anger and frustration. I knew my parents loved me, but neither one of them ever uttered those words. Having Chad love me felt like a warm blanket being wrapped around me. It felt really good.

Now, here I sat, three years later, alone on a park bench trying to decide how I would end my life.

If Chad didn't want to be with me, and he didn't love me anymore, I didn't want to be on this planet any longer. I truly felt that I couldn't live without him. As I became all-consumed in my misery, I began to cry uncontrollably.

Bent over, my face in my hands, tears pouring down my face, an image caught my attention out of the corner of my eye. Seated directly beside me was an elderly white-haired man with his hand extended. He was attempting to hand me a handkerchief. He didn't say a word. I was shocked that he was there. How did he get here? Where did he come from? Why didn't I hear him approaching the bench? It was the most bizarre experience. I looked around, and there wasn't another person within sight.

Reluctantly, I grabbed the handkerchief. My face was covered in tears, and my nose was running. As I unfolded the handkerchief, I could see words embroidered across one side. It read: *If you want your life to change, you must change.*

Chapter 2

"Keep it," the stranger said as I dried my tears and blew my nose.

I couldn't imagine that he would have wanted his handkerchief back anyway. The thought of giving it back didn't seem appropriate, considering what I was using it for.

Although having this person sitting beside me was an unexpected surprise, I felt a strange sense of comfort, knowing he remained seated there. I was touched by the generosity of this stranger. The cotton of the handkerchief happened to be the finest and softest material I had ever touched. I wondered who embroidered the saying. *If you want your life to change, you must change.*

In that moment, I began to ponder whether this message was somehow meant specifically for me.

I thanked him, and then quietly asked his name.

He replied, "My name is Savy." He extended his hand. "It is a pleasure to meet you."

"Savy? That's an unusual name. My name is Sophie." I reached out and shook his hand. He had the softest hands, yet his handshake was firm and warm.

"What brings you to the park so early in the morning, young lady?" he asked.

In the fleeting seconds between his question and my answer, I wondered whether I should tell him the truth or give him some other acceptable answer. I decided to tell the truth. After all, I had never met this man before and wasn't sure if I'd ever see him again. What could it hurt to tell him the real reason for sitting on that park bench on this autumn morning?

"I came here to figure out how I would end my life," I responded slowly and quietly as I reconnected to my sadness.

He responded without skipping a beat. "Interesting. What did you decide?"

His response and question mystified me. He asked with great enthusiasm. Is he supportive of this idea? Does he think it is okay for a person to take their own life? I wondered if perhaps he had thought the same thing at one point.

As we sat inches apart on this bench, I began to study him carefully.

Savy was a tall and slender man, and he was dressed impeccably in casual clothes. It was obvious his clothes were made of the finest materials and purchased at a store where they sell high-end designer clothes. His shoes, although appearing comfortable, looked as though they had been shined that morning. I could actually see reflections in the patent leather. His pants were a khaki color and had a perfect pleat down the front. His beautiful light-brown cashmere sweater was partially hidden underneath a beige jacket that looked warm and stylish.

With a full head of white, thick wavy hair, his hairstyle happened to be combed back, and there wasn't a single strand out of place. He wore glasses, and the side of his glasses exposed the double G emblem for Gucci. When he had extended his hand with the handkerchief, I also noted he had a Rolex watch, and on his left ring finger, he wore a gold wedding band. By his appearance, it certainly looked like he had money.

While contemplating his question, I reflected upon the ideas that I had been considering to end my life. Would I take some of my mom's sleeping pills that I discovered months ago in her medicine cabinet? Would I slit my wrists? Would I jump off the bridge on the highway? Maybe I could try the same approach my mom took when I was fourteen.

My parents had been going through a rough time. I wasn't familiar with all of the details, but I was exposed to the fighting. I heard my mom tell my dad how upset she was to discover he had a child with another woman. I suspect for years, my father was having extramarital affairs, and although my mom knew about them, she felt stuck.

She finally reached a breaking point and felt she couldn't go on. She cut the garden hose and put one end in the exhaust pipe of the car and inserted the other end in the slat of a partially opened window. She closed the garage door and started the car.

Fortunately, my dad found her in time to save her.

In my mind, I considered all options for ending my life and was determined to do it either that day or the next.

I finally answered his question. "Nah, not yet."

For the next few moments, we sat in silence.

Savy broke the quietness by saying, "You know Sophie, you are in a dark place at this moment. When you are in a dark place, similar to being in a dark room, you can't see. You are not seeing the many options that are available to you. You can't see your way out, but if you shift your focus slightly, you will start to see the light."

His words were delivered with genuine sincerity and conviction. He wasn't attempting to be someone who was preaching. I received his message with the intention it was sent . . . with gentle, caring, authentic love.

Savy continued. "What if you chose to look at your life in a totally different way? What if you choose to focus on what is great in your life rather than focusing on what is wrong? What is one thing in your life that is great right now? I am confident there are many things in your life that are great, but for the sake of this moment, share one thing with me."

This series of questions definitely interrupted my sadness. I felt an internal tug-of-war going on within me. One side was attempting to pull me back into the gloom and doom and deep sadness; the other side was encouraging me to heed Savy's question and to consider another way of thinking.

Similar to watching the sun rise in the morning and seeing the light peak over the horizon, I felt a ray of sunshine coming into my heart.

With a gentle yet firm voice, Savy added, "Sophie, your decision to end your life is a serious decision. Plus, if you follow through, there is no turning back. It would be my recommendation that you give this very serious consideration as all of your decisions have a ripple effect."

"Ripple effect? What do you mean?"

"A great gift that you have been given from birth is the gift of choice. You get to choose what you are going to focus on. You get to choose what thoughts you allow to enter into your mind, and believe it or not, you get to choose how you feel at any moment."

"Whoa whoa whoa!" I interrupted. "Wait a minute, Mr. Savy. You have no idea what I've been through in my life. You don't even know me. You really know nothing about me. How can you say this with such conviction when you know nothing about me?"

"Sophie, it really doesn't matter what you've been through. You have an opportunity right now in this very moment to make a new decision. Just like you can't change the time you got out of bed this morning, you can't do anything about the past; but you can learn from it. You have the opportunity, in this very moment, to look at things differently. You can choose to see your life as the gift that it is. You can choose to see the experiences in your life as the stepping-stones to greatness."

I drifted back to thinking about the ripple effect of me ending my life. I was deeply concerned about my mom; she had been emotionally fragile. I wondered how my death would impact her. Would it destroy her? Would she also lose the will to live?

This was the only thing stopping me from moving forward at this time. I found myself more concerned about my mom's potential pain than I was about my own. My mom had been through a lot in her life.

Savy stood up. "Sophie, I would like you to make me two promises, please. Promise me you will meet me here next Thursday at the exact same time. Also, promise me that between now and then, you will look for the good in every situation and find the greatness."

I thought about his request for a moment. Savy was asking me to be there in one week. This meant that I would still be alive. That felt incredibly painful. The freshness of my breakup with Chad was still so strong. My heart felt heavy. I felt all consumed in emotional pain. I wasn't seeing a way out . . . or was Savy helping me look at my life differently?

Was this a life preserver? And would I take it?

Reluctantly, I replied, "Okay, I promise."

Chapter 3

As I headed back home, I realized that the school bus had already picked up the others in our neighborhood a good fifteen minutes earlier.

"Shoot," I said aloud. "How am I going to get to school now?"

An idea entered my mind. Sharon, who lived next door from me, had her own car, and she drove herself to and from school every day. Maybe if I hurried, I could catch a ride with her. We had exchanged phone numbers a year earlier when she moved into the neighborhood, and even though we never really hung out, we were always pleasant with each other. Most of my spare time was spent with Chad or my best friend Becca or working at the local grocery store as a cashier. Sharon seemed to be a loner. She studied a lot and seemed to be somewhat socially awkward.

As I rounded the corner to my home, I noticed Sharon's car was still parked in her driveway.

I raced in the front door of my home and headed to the phone that hung on the wall in the kitchen. All of our neighbors' telephone numbers were listed on the small whiteboard located directly beside the phone. My parents had left for work more than an hour earlier, and my older sister Brandy must have caught the school bus.

I dialed Sharon's number, and within one ring, she answered. She told me that she would be leaving in fifteen minutes and she would be happy to give me a ride to school.

As I sat in the passenger seat of Sharon's car and we approached the school, I began to feel anxious. On the drive to school, Sharon and I were casually talking about the unusually warm weather for this time of year and exchanging pleasantries. For a few moments, I completely forgot that I would be seeing Chad in the hallway, and unlike other days, we wouldn't be walking hand in hand or sharing lunch or after-school time together.

I began focusing on Chad and our breakup. I felt a surge of emotions rise up within me, and, similar to a volcano, I wondered if I would erupt into a stream of tears at any moment.

And then, something weird happened. All of a sudden, Savy's words came to my mind: "Focus on what is great in your life, Sophie!"

I started to give this serious consideration as he advised. "What's great in my life?" I asked myself.

Nothing! Nothing at all. The love of my life ended our relationship, and I don't want to live!"

I stopped that stream of thinking, considering how people outside my circumstance might find those thoughts absurd, and I began to reflect on the great things in my life. I mentally made a list.

I am grateful to be alive.

I am grateful Sharon gave me a ride to school.

I am grateful to have met Savy in the park this morning.

I am grateful for my family, even though we fight most of the time.

I am grateful for my eyesight (although this one feels like a stretch).

I am grateful for my friends.

As that last thought entered my mind, I started to wonder if Becca and I would remain best friends. After all, she was dating Chad's brother Danny and the majority of the time we hung out together was as a foursome.

The great tug-of-war of emotions continued. One moment, I found myself focusing on the breakup and my sadness—and a moment later, focusing on what is great in my life. My emotions felt like they were in a ping-pong match.

The sheer fact that I was choosing to focus on some of the things that are great in my life did begin to change how I was feeling. If I would just stick to this, perhaps I could turn the corner of negative feelings.

For the first time ever, I began to become the observer of my own thoughts and had the realization that my thoughts are not *me*.

This felt so unusual; however, I began to feel a bit more free.

A week passed without any major emotional breakdowns. I did see Chad in the hallways, and we traded glances, but the sting of the relationship breakup was still very deep within my heart.

I would catch a glimpse of him from afar, and my heart would skip a beat. It hurt me to see him. I missed him. I missed holding his hand walking to class. I missed our closeness. Not having Chad in my life felt like a huge void. In some ways, I felt lost.

One of my friends told me that Chad started to see another girl. Thankfully, she attended a different school, which meant I wouldn't be seeing them together. Nonetheless, the pain was very real.

Becca promised me that the breakup with Chad would not impact our friendship whatsoever. In her words, "We are friends for life." Becca's compassion comforted me.

One week had come and gone with what seemed like the blink of an eye.

Thursday morning came, and it was time to go and meet Savy in the park. Would he really show up again?

I found myself genuinely excited to see him. I hardly knew this man, but there was something about his presence that felt comforting.

Dressing warmly and appropriately for the cooler weather, I raced out at 6:20 a.m. to get to the park on time. Fortunately, my parents had already left for work, so it wasn't necessary to go into any explanation for my reason for going to the park at this time of the day. My sister never really paid any attention to me, and vice versa, so I wasn't even concerned about what she would think or say.

As I approached the park bench under the willow tree, I could see that Savy was already there.

"Good morning, sunshine!" Savy said with great enthusiasm.

"Hi, Savy," I replied.

Without hesitation, he dove right in. "So, tell me, did you focus on the great things in your life this past week?"

"Savy, I have to be honest with you. It was not easy. I had one heck of a time finding the good things in my life or finding the greatness, especially when I found myself in the depths of despair. I did, however, begin a new ritual . . . a daily ritual that has really helped me."

"Oh?" he inquired. "Do tell."

"Inspired by the promise I made to you last week, I started a journal. I call it my GIMY journal. GIMY stands for *Great In My Life*. Every day I write in it what I'm grateful for. I've found it shifts my thoughts and feelings away from what isn't great, and it causes me to feel better. I carry my journal everywhere with me and write in it throughout the day."

"Better is a good word, Sophie. Finding the seeds of greatness and being grateful is a powerful way to change how you feel and to attract to you better results."

I stopped him. "Huh? I am sorry, but I don't understand what you mean." What Savy said sounded like Greek to me (and with my straight D grades, I definitely didn't speak Greek).

Savy went on to explain. "Being grateful is an emotional state of mind that puts you in harmony with positive emotions, and when you are feeling good, you attract good. Gratitude is an attitude, and the attitude in which you fill your days has a direct impact on the kind of life you have and the direction you take your life."

"Okay, I think I get it now. Thank you, Savy. Your advice has already made a big difference in my life. But I do still feel a bit lost. I honestly don't know what to do with myself. I used to spend most of my time with Chad, and he's no longer in my life, and I don't know what to do."

Still feeling a bit emotional, I had blurted out what seemed to be my current biggest struggle. I sensed that Savy was a man with answers and great wisdom, and I felt I could trust him.

"Sophie, what are you most passionate about?"

"Passionate about? Let me think about that."

Savy went on to explain, "When you are in emotional pain or feeling lost, you have an opportunity to connect to something meaningful in order to bring your attention to higher ground. When answering what you are passionate about, there is no right or wrong answer—it is *your* answer. So, think for a moment. What is something that you are really passionate about? What do you love? What are you interested in? What inspires you?"

Savy was, yet again, asking some valuable, thought-provoking questions. These are questions that I had never even thought of before. I instantly started to wonder if, at my age, it was even necessary or important to focus on that. After all, I was a high school student. What does passion have to do with high school?

It was almost as if he was reading my mind as he continued.

"Passion is the burning feeling inside of you to *do* something, to *have* something, to *experience* something, or to *be* something that you've never done before. Passion is the fuel that propels you to success."

Savy glanced at his watch. "Sophie, I can't meet with you next Thursday, but how about if we meet one month from today on the same bench, and you can share with me what you are passionate about? Are you open to doing that? And, Sophie, I suggest you ponder this as if your life depends on it because it does."

He smiled, and I could feel his honesty as if it was radiating from his core.

I agreed to meet with Savy in a month, and we went our separate ways.

As I started to walk away, I came to the realization that I knew nothing about this man! Who was he? Where did he come from? What did he do for a living? Did he have a family? I became so curious to know these answers. In time, perhaps it would all become crystal clear to me.

Chapter 4

The questions Savy asked me to focus on had me deeply thinking.

I had never really thought about my passions before. I had been far more aware of what I was *not* passionate about rather than what I felt a passion for.

School was not something I felt a passion for. I found school to be a total bore, and the teachers often ticked me off. I really despised being told what to do and when to do it. Homework? Forget it. I rarely did homework, and I never studied for tests. Amazingly enough, I did manage to pass each and every grade, but there were times when I wasn't sure if I was going to pass my grade or not. My focus in school was to get the minimum grade to pass. Unlike my sister Brandy, who was a straight-A and honor student, I felt school was a total waste of my time.

Brandy was in the five-year program at the high school. When entering high school, students were given the option to enroll in a four-year program or a five-year program. The students who graduated from the five-year program had a better chance of getting into university. There was no desire within me to continue school after high school. After all, I really detested being there at all. So I entered the four-year program.

Cheerleading was something that was fun and enjoyable. However, I had to ask myself if this was my passion. It became clear to me that cheerleading had been only a way to be closer to my boyfriend, and that part of my life had now dramatically changed.

Working as a cashier at a grocery store wasn't my passion either, although I sure enjoyed receiving my weekly pay.

So, what was I passionate about?

Sports? Nope.

Gardening? Definitely not.

Cooking? Not for me.

History? Boring.

Travel? I never really gave that much thought. I loved to ride my bike, but cycling didn't categorize as a passion, at least not for me.

Feeling frustrated that I wasn't connecting to my passion, I decided to go to the park after school and sit on the familiar bench, thinking that I may get inspired. It had been three weeks since my last rendezvous with Savy, and we were scheduled to meet the following Thursday morning.

The school day typically ended around 3:10 p.m., and the buses arrived at 3:30 p.m. to take us all home. On this particular day, after jumping off the school bus, I raced home to throw my backpack in the entranceway and head to the park.

The weather was getting cooler by the day. Dressed warmly, I headed to what became known as my 'thinking place.'

Cooler weather definitely kept the activity in the park to a minimum, although there were a couple of dog walkers and a young mother pushing her baby in a stroller all bundled up as if it was the middle of winter. *Better safe and warm than sorry*, I thought.

After I sat on the bench, I relaxed, took a deep breath, and closed my eyes to focus. I began to reflect on my passions. I asked myself the question slowly over and over again. What am I passionate about? What am I passionate about? What am I passionate about? I paused and reflected each time I asked.

And then finally, out of nowhere, like a bolt of lightning, it hit me: I am passionate about writing. I would love to be a writer!

In school, I was barely getting by. If a D grade was a passing grade, I would work toward getting a D, just enough to pass. However, there was one class that I loved, and that was my English class.

I was passionate about writing stories. I loved learning about the principles of writing, literature, and grammar. I had become passionate about reading as well, and I was a regular at the local library, taking out books to read every single week. Oftentimes my face was buried in a book when other family members watched the regular sitcoms on television in the evening.

Even before I opened my eyes, I felt someone coming toward me. I turned in the direction of this presence, and to my surprise, I realized it was Savy.

Eagerly, I jumped up. "Savy! What are you doing here? We aren't meeting until next Thursday, so why are you here today, at this time?" I asked.

"Hey, Sophie. My intuition guided me to come to the park today. I always listen to my intuition, especially when the messages are strong and clear. I don't question these intuitive messages. I just act on them."

"Regardless of why you are here or what prompted you to be here, I'm grateful you are. You see Savy? I said I am grateful. Did you hear that?" I chuckled and continued. I was so excited. I didn't even give him a chance to respond.

"Your advice, from the first day we met, has impacted me and stayed with me, and I now find myself focusing on the great things in my life every single day. I'm truly grateful for you, Savy."

"I am grateful for you too, Sophie," Savy said with a smile. "I think it is fabulous that you took my advice and integrated it into your life, and you continue to. Change takes time, discipline, and commitment. And, there's an old saying that goes like this: 'You can lead a horse to water, but you can't make him drink.' Well, Sophie, I am proud of you for choosing to drink the water."

I smiled even wider. "Hey Savy, guess what?"

"Let me see," he said as he looked up into the sky, playfully appearing to be searching for an answer. "Oh, I know. You have discovered what you are passionate about. Is that accurate?"

"Yes!" I exclaimed. "I sure did. I am passionate about writing."

"Great, and what would you love to do with that passion?" he asked, staring into my eyes, waiting for an answer.

"I dunno. Write?" I laughed, offering my simple and quick answer, shrugging my shoulders.

"Sophie, think about what you would love as far as outcomes are concerned. In other words, if you could do anything as a writer and accomplish anything, what would you love for that to be?"

"Hmm . . . great question, Savy. I will have to think about this," I responded. "You always give me something to think about!"

"Sophie, we are scheduled to be together next Thursday morning at this same location. How about if you come here with a clear intention regarding your writing. Consider that question 'What would you love?' and come here prepared to give me your answer. But I do want to give you one more piece of advice, and this is likely going to be one of the most critical pieces of advice I will ever give to you. Are you ready?"

"Ready, Freddy!" I playfully answered with a big grin on my face. While my demeanor was a bit giddy, I seriously prepared my mind to soak up whatever he was about to say like a sponge.

"When you begin to consider the outcomes that you would love, please know that you do not have to know HOW you will accomplish them. Forget the HOW or the WAY because they can make your desired outcome seem impossible. Trust me when I say that you can do whatever you wish, no matter how lofty the ideas may seem. So, connect only to the outcome of what you desire. Don't worry about the rest. Understand?" Savy asked.

"Yep. I get it. Thank you, Savy. I'm looking forward to when we meet again. I better get home for dinner now—see you very soon." My words trailed off as I got up to head home. I couldn't wait to complete Savy's latest exercise. I could feel momentum building as if something special was about to happen.

Savy smiled, waved, and headed in the opposite direction.

There was a bounce in my step as I walked home. I hadn't felt this excited in a long time. In fact, I honestly couldn't recall ever feeling this motivated.

Chapter 5

The walk back home from the park that day was a unique one. I found myself skipping joyfully along the road. This was the first time in my life that I felt a genuine sense of anticipation for the future.

I arrived home before my parents. It was my turn to make dinner. I immediately began preparing the meal.

My parents both worked full time. My dad worked as a janitor at the town hall, and because he didn't feel he earned enough to cover all of our expenses, he worked two other office-cleaning jobs to earn extra money.

Every day my dad left home to go to work at 6 a.m. and returned at 7 or 8 o'clock in the evening. He always seemed to have an enormous amount of energy, though. After working a long day, Dad would arrive home, eat dinner, and often head straight into another project—whether he was working in his greenhouse that he built in the backyard or making improvements to our home.

Mom worked at a factory, and the work she did was grueling and physically exhausting. She left for work every morning minutes after my dad and quite often didn't return home until 6 p.m. Mom returned home every evening, completely wiped out and emotionally drained. I believe Mom and Dad were happy to have their two daughters home to prepare meals every night.

My two older brothers were living on their own. Both were married and had small children.

My brother Braden was eight years older than me, and he moved out when he was sixteen years old. Braden and my parents didn't get along very well when he lived at home. Once he moved out, got a job, settled down, and began his own family, his relationship strengthened with my parents.

My relationship with Braden was always a strong one. We were close and talked often.

My brother Clancy was only three years older than me, and he married at the young age of eighteen and became a father by the time he was nineteen.

Both of my brothers had two children, a boy and a girl. I loved my nieces and nephews and looked forward to their visit every Sunday when Mom would cook and bake up a storm. I believed my mom loved cooking and baking and, more importantly, she loved her family. She became an amazing grandma: attentive, playful, and always giving plenty of love to the grandkids when they visited.

I often wondered why she was such a loving grandma yet appeared to be an unaffectionate mom. I recalled one time my mom told me that her mother was much the same way: not affectionate with her own children, but overly affectionate with the grandchildren. I guess in her case, the apple didn't fall far from the tree.

Savy's recommendation to find the things in my life that are great helped me to focus on the wonderful aspects of my family as well. While I previously took these family Sundays for granted, now my feelings of gratitude for them were smack dab in the middle of my awareness, and it really made a difference.

Carrying my GIMY journal around all day, I found myself writing notes spontaneously. I was feeling calmer, less confrontational, experiencing less anger, and I was definitely feeling more confident.

I reflected on the conversation I had with Savy about the ripple effect of actions and felt strongly that the ripple effect of focus also had some positive benefits. For example, because I shifted my focus away from the things that upset me, I discovered the gifts and the blessings in my life. My focus became primarily on the great things in my life—a stark contrast from focusing on what wasn't so great. As a result, I felt better about myself. It's shocking how much a simple shift in my thinking and focus made in the enjoyment of my life.

I even felt somewhat healed from the relationship breakup with Chad and had started a new friendship with a guy from my school named Eddie. Eddie's name was Jonathan Edwards, but his closest friends called him Eddie. Eddie and I met in ninth grade and, unbeknownst to me, he had feelings for me from the day we met. I had no idea he was interested in me. How could I have possibly known when my attention was fixated on Chad!

My relationship with Eddie was developing at a slow pace, which is precisely how I desired it to advance. Eddie was very patient with me, and I appreciated that. I continued to feel sad for the breakup with Chad, but as time went on, my sadness lessened.

My confidence was growing, and everything in my life appeared brighter.

Before I knew it, it was the day of my meeting with my mysterious new friend Savy. At 6:20 a.m., I busted out the door, heading to our special meeting place.

This time I carried a backpack with me, filled with two journals, a pen, and a highlighter. I wanted to show

Savy my journals and also to take notes, as I knew he'd surely have more wisdom to share with me.

This time I arrived at the park before Savy. However, minutes later, I saw him coming around the corner.

He was like a bright beam of light. He had an aura about him that seemed to radiate—I mean, I didn't even know what an aura was, and I certainly didn't read them, but his was unmistakable even to someone like me. He walked with certainty. I don't think I noticed any of this before, but it was visibly obvious this morning.

It was a much colder morning; however, we were both bundled up to handle the weather. The thought did occur to me that if these rendezvous were going to continue, we had to find a warmer place to meet next time!

Savy, in his usual way, not wasting a moment, got straight to business. "Good morning, Sophie. Please tell me what your answer is to that powerful four-word question: 'What would you love?'"

Reaching into my backpack, I pulled out my journals and began my response. "Savy, I have my GIMY journal, and now I have my WILY journal. The GIMY journal you are already familiar with. It's my *Great In My*

Life journal. The WILY journal is my *What I Would Love* journal."

I felt an affection for my journals by giving them these fun names, and I believe Savy was somewhat amused!

"Savy, what I would love is to be a world-famous author with millions and millions of my books sold all over the world, translated into many languages, and enjoying the praise from readers who love my books."

I said these words with such pride. I actually surprised myself as I was saying them because I didn't realize how good it felt to say this out loud. Up until this point, it was my little secret.

"And Savy, you did tell me that I didn't need to be concerned about the *how*, right? How I'll do all of this?"

"That's absolutely right, Sophie," he said with confidence and a smile. "I love this vision, and I believe you will accomplish this if and when you truly connect to the knowing that *it is already done*."

"Wait a minute! What did you just say? I don't understand what you mean by that. Please help me understand."

"Sophie, the way to manifest this passion into your life is to feel as if you have already accomplished it. In other words, you live your life AS IF, as if you are already the success that you desire to be."

"But I'm a high school student! I'm not an author yet. I haven't written a single page. I don't have an agent. I don't even know if I can write good." I uttered these words, intentionally using bad grammar.

"Listen up, Sophie. You remember the last time we met, and I told you that you don't have to know HOW you will accomplish this?"

"Yes, of course," I answered. "You also told me that it happened to be one of the most valuable lessons I would ever learn."

"The process of manifestation involves three very powerful steps. When you follow these steps, you will discover that you can truly experience anything you desire. I see you have your pen and paper ready, so here's something you are definitely going to want to write down. Ready for the three steps?" Savy asked.

"Let 'er rip, Skip!" I said, chuckling as the words were coming out of my mouth.

Savy began to speak, and honestly, it sounded like a serenade.

"Step 1. Decide what you would love. Commit your goal to paper by writing it down. And, when you write your goal down, write it down as if you have already accomplished it using only *present tense* words and add some *emotion* to your statement.

"For example, you could say something like this: *I am so happy and so very grateful to be an international best-selling successful award-winning author with millions of books sold and books translated into many languages.*

"Be certain that your goal statement allows you to see the end result as well. You see it in your mind's eye."

I feverishly wrote everything down as fast as I could.

He continued.

"Step 2. Determine what you need to *believe* and *feel* when you have accomplished this goal. This is where your paradigms are formed.

"Paradigms are a set of beliefs that determine how you think, speak, act, and feel. Your paradigms are part of your subconscious mind, which is thirty-thousand times more powerful than your conscious, thinking mind. Thirty-thousand times, Sophie!"

I was intrigued.

"For example, you may determine these beliefs are necessary for your goal to be manifested in your life—in fact, write these down as I say them:

I am a world-class, phenomenal writer who has a gift with words.

I am deserving of success.

I accomplish everything I set my mind to.

Readers love my books and tell their friends.

I have now sold millions and millions of copies of my books."

"You got that?" he asked.

Laughing and still writing like a maniac, I replied, "I'm trying!"

He finished his instructions with this.

"And finally, Step 3. Feel it. Feel it now. Feel your success fully. Embrace those feelings as if you are living that life right now— not sometime in the future, but right now.

"The secret to manifesting anything you desire is to feel *as if it is here now*. This is the step where most people get tripped up because it almost feels like they're lying to themselves, so they resist doing it. You see, many people understand these principles—they know what they should be doing, but they don't do it. They continue to feel *lack*. They continue to feel frustration. They look at outside conditions and results—like the fact that you haven't even written a word yet—and they allow this to determine how they feel. Therein, they connect to emotional states that are destructive, like fear and doubt. They self-sabotage all of the time. So, Sophie, you must be strong, focused, and extremely disciplined."

Savy's instructions sounded simple enough. I seemed to understand every word he was saying as if I suddenly could speak a long-forgotten language. I felt confident I could follow these three simple steps.

"Thank you, Savy. This seems like a very simple recipe for success. Would that be accurate?" I asked.

"Simple? Yes! Easy, not so much," he replied.

"Listen, humans are habitual by nature. People tend to do the same things over and over and over again. Even though you are at a young age in your life now, your paradigms have already been formed—many of them were formed by the time you were six years of age.

"The good news is that you can change them. And you must understand it usually takes time. When you are working on changing your paradigms—your beliefs, recognize that the old beliefs will attempt to keep you where you are now. With discipline, focus, and commitment, you can replace these old paradigms with new paradigms. And of utmost importance is for you to follow the recommendation from Step 3.

"Every day, you must conduct yourself as the person who has already accomplished that goal. Quite often, this exercise is done within your conscious mind. You focus on your outcome, and you hold it with your will. Your will is another one of your mental faculties that allows you to hold your attention. You create the result first inside your imagination and then take action in the so-called real world that matches what you already did inside your imagination. This can be challenging, especially at first, so learn to love the thing called your will."

Miraculously, I felt as though I really got what Savy was telling me.

"Sounds like I have more work to do, Savy. I respect that, and I'm ready for it. I'm so grateful for your instructions, and I'm in love with my goal—and I really do believe it's possible for me."

These words were shared with such confidence that I honestly felt that someone else had taken over my body and voice. It reminded me of the first time I started to become the observer of my thoughts, yet this time these words seemed to come from outside of—or beyond—me.

"Sophie, you are a very smart young lady. I do believe you will accomplish this *when* you stay committed to it. This is going to take some time, though, and you must be patient. You will also come up against challenges and adversity. You have to be mentally and emotionally strong. You have already started a positive discipline with your GIMY journal—I love that, and you should keep that up as it will help you."

Savy continued, "Let's meet again in one month and see where you are and how you are doing. Sound good to you? We may need to really bundle up warm, though, as we are about to enter into the winter months, but if you are game for meeting in the park one month from today at the same time, I will be here."

"You've got it! It's a date," I replied.

Minutes later, we were both on our way back to our respective homes, although the thought crossed my mind again. Where does Savy live? I still don't know anything about him.

I was deeply grateful I met Savy as his wisdom was changing my life for the better. I had never felt more invigorated. I found myself feeling good most of the time, and my grades were rising at school for the first time in my life. I was feeling optimistic about my life, and Eddie and I were enjoying each other's company. Humorously, I thought that maybe I should start to wear shades, as I felt my future was very bright.

My mind was deep in thought until I realized I had exactly three minutes to catch my bus, so I began to run to get to the corner of the street on time. I made it as the bus was approaching. My sister was standing there looking at me with a bewildered look on her face, and her arm extended, demonstrating to me she had my school backpack. She may have been wondering where I came from. She handed me my backpack without uttering a word or asking any questions.

Chapter 6

It had been one month since the last time I saw Savy. I found myself thinking about the positive changes already occurring in my life, including how much better and optimistic I felt about life and the observable improvement in my grades. Even my teachers made comments about the enhancement in my attitude.

I felt this insatiable appetite desiring for more of what I started calling "Savy wisdom." Having to wait a month to see him again felt like a long time, although it did give me time to make some serious progress.

Savy awakened a side of me that I didn't even realize was there. I felt more alive than I ever felt in my life. I desired to live a life of my choice rather than the miserable, impoverished one that both my parents seemed to be living. It's like an entirely different world opened up.

My parents both came from families who struggled financially, and therefore, they learned how to struggle too. My mom's parents arrived in Canada from Italy and, upon arrival, didn't speak a word of English. Not only did they need to learn a new language, but they also had to find a way to support their family in a new country.

After settling in, my grandparents had twelve children, and the effort to clothe, feed, and house all of these children was an enormous undertaking. My grandmother was a stay-at-home mom, and my grandfather was a bricklayer, earning enough for them to purchase a small home in the city of Toronto. My grandfather died of a massive stroke a couple of weeks after my brother Clancy was born, which meant, sadly, I never got to meet him.

My dad's parents came from England (my grandmother) and Scotland (my grandfather). However, when my dad's mom was pregnant with my dad, my grandfather died unexpectedly. She was uneducated, unestablished. She had no source of income and two other young children. It was incredibly challenging for my grandmother to deal with her husband's unexpected death and find a way to earn a living, but she somehow managed (barely) to make ends meet.

I recall my dad telling me that he didn't have a proper bed to sleep in, so he put together a large garbage bag of rags so that he had something soft to rest on. He also told me that he and his brother and sister were often extremely hungry. In order to eat, he would steal bread off the delivery truck that delivered groceries in their neighborhood.

His mother became an alcoholic and would go to the local pub in the afternoon and drink until she could barely walk. Her children were at home, fending for themselves.

We were fortunate to have a home and a roof over our heads, but I found that my parents often argued, and the majority of their disagreements were over money, or rather, the lack of it.

Also, when my siblings or I wanted to have something, and we asked for it, our parents would yell at us in angry tones and say things like, "Who do you think you are?" or "What do you think, money grows on trees?" Based on our other relatives and friends, their families seemed to struggle too. So, it appeared to be the norm.

Something inside me felt that it didn't have to be that way. I observed other families who lived in nicer homes, wore more elegant clothes, and drove luxurious cars. In fact, in our hometown of Bridlewood, there was a section of town with expensive high-end homes surrounding a large man-made lake. One particular home really stood out. Apparently, the rumor was that a multi-billionaire lived in this massive house.

This home had a large stone fence around the entire property. It appeared castle-like, with turrets. I often wondered who lived in that mansion and what they did for a living to be able to live like that.

At an early age, I learned the value of earning money, and I loved earning it. When I was old enough to help my dad with some of his cleaning jobs, I would go with him, and he would pay me with cash. During the summer months off school, my mom would take me to work at the factory, and I worked full time for those eight weeks. I absolutely loved receiving that envelope at the end of the week stuffed with a small pile of cash.

At fourteen years of age, the legal age to start employment, I managed to secure a part-time job at the local grocery store, and throughout high school, I maintained this job. One of the things that I loved most about this job was the interaction with the customers. It was fun work, most of the time.

I started saving money very early, and by the time I was approaching my eighteenth birthday and in my final year of high school, I had enough money to buy a used car, pay the insurance, and pay for the gas. The idea of having a car represented freedom: the freedom to come and go as I pleased, of course, all the while respecting the rules of my parent's home.

As it turned out, my brother Clancy's wife, Allison, decided to buy herself a new car and put her used vehicle up for sale. It was a six-year-old Buick Skylark and had very low mileage. She offered it to me at an attractive price, and I jumped on it. Now I had my own wheels and felt like one of the cool kids at school.

Even though my life was somewhat busy with school, cheerleading, helping out at home, working part-time at the grocery store, and sporadic dates with my new boyfriend Eddie, I managed to carve out time to work on my assignment. How couldn't I? I was so jazzed about where my life as an author was headed!

Savy had provided wonderful guidance in our last meeting, instructing me on the three steps to manifest any desire. As a result of his recommendations, I invested a significant amount of time working on my goals, something I had never done before meeting him.

As I wrote goal after goal after goal, I was in the spirit of I CAN DO ANYTHING AND I DON'T HAVE TO KNOW HOW. Those may not have been the exact words of advice from Savy, but that became my interpretation, and I was writing down some pretty wild and crazy goals. As far as I was concerned, there was no limit to what I could do, be, have, and experience. I believed it because I knew Savy did.

My meeting day with Savy finally arrived. With excitement, I sprung out of bed, quickly dressed, stuffed my journals into my backpack, and raced off to the park. This time I wasn't as concerned about catching the bus because I had my own car to drive myself to and from school. Oddly enough, my sister Brandy still took the bus. I think she liked to socialize with the other kids on the bus, and her boyfriend Steve lived on the bus route, so she sat with him.

As Savy approached, he could see that I had all of my journals spread out across the park bench. I had my GIMY journal (*Great In My Life*), my WILY journal (*What I Would Love*), and now my new *Scripts and Beliefs* journal that I affectionately called SABY.

"Well, well, young lady, what do we have here?" Savy asked with curiosity.

I reminded him of the first two journals and immediately showed him my new journal.

"Savy, this is my SABY journal. Not Savy but SABY." I giggled.

"Last time we met, you explained the second step to manifestation. I made a decision to invest the time to really dive deep into establishing what necessary beliefs are required to manifest my desires. I began describing what my feelings would be when these goals have manifested. As a result, I created a number of written statements of my beliefs, with detailed descriptions, or in other words, scripts."

"Wow, Sophie, it looks like you are taking this seriously," Savy commented with a smile on his face.

"You said my life depended on it. You meant that, right?"

"Yes, definitely." Savy went on, "Most people tiptoe their way through life hoping they'll make it safely to death. The truth is, life isn't a rehearsal or preparedness for something else, for some other lifetime. Life is happening now. There isn't a trial run, and you don't get any do-overs. This is it! It is time to make the most of it. You see, I was blessed to have a very wise friend who took the time to explain how life works to me. When I was quite young, my friend told me that magic is the opposite of life. He said that with magic when you know how it works, the magic disappears; however, with life, when you know how it works, the magic begins."

"Hold on, hold on, I wanna write that down." I repeated his words as I wrote: "With magic when you know how it works, the magic disappears. With life, when you know how it works, the magic begins. Dang Savy, that is profound."

Savy smiled at my enthusiasm for his words.

When Savy spoke, he seemed to be having an out-of-body experience. It appeared that something or someone took over. Maybe a spirit entered his physical body or something—I honestly don't know—but it was mesmerizing to watch.

"Sophie, it is important to understand there is tremendous power locked within you. You are now tapping into that power and bringing out a greater and grander version of who you are by the actions you are taking. It is important now to continue to expand in awareness. When you expand your awareness, your understanding intensifies. In Proverbs, in the Bible, it states: 'Wisdom is the principal thing; therefore, get wisdom and in all thy getting, get understanding.'

"You see, the secret to life is to feel joy and freedom while continuously holding the intention of what you want. Even though it may not be in your life at the moment and there may not be any evidence of it in sight, stay connected to what you would love as if it is already here. That's how you draw what you want to you. By doing this, you activate the life-affirming power within you.

"This power can take over your life. It will guide you, protect you, direct you, and sustain your very existence if you let it. And you will achieve a miraculous experience of life."

I sat there in stunned silence, rigorously taking notes. I started to ask myself how I became so lucky to have met this incredible, wise elderly man. Was this destiny? Months ago, in my moment of contemplation about giving everything up—life itself—I seem to have found the very secrets of life.

I loved the many things I was learning from Savy. I decided to remain open to create a deeper understanding.

"Savy, I have to get to school, but when can we meet again? I would really love to see you again."

"What would you love, Sophie?" he asked with a grin on his face.

"One month from now, we will be in full-blown Christmas mode, and exams are happening between then and now, so how about we meet up in the new year? Would the first of January work for you, same time, same place? The dress code is winter woollys, and I can bring a thermos of coffee!"

"We're on. See you in the new year. May you be blessed with a magical Christmas, Sophie. All the best to you and your family," Savy said sincerely.

"Same to you!" My voice trailed off as I raced to my car.

Chapter 7

The month of December was upon us. I loved this time of year. Not only because it was Christmastime, but it was also my birthday on the nineteenth. The spirit of the holidays pulsated with joy and merriment. This jubilant energy could be felt everywhere. People smiled and were friendlier and kinder. Children behaved better because they knew Santa was coming. Shoppers were overflowing in the stores.

My parents always made Christmas special for us kids. Even though they didn't have much money, they managed to buy us lots of gifts. We loved that.

My brothers and their families planned to join us on Christmas Eve and Christmas Day. It was fun to have my nieces and nephews over as the young ones definitely brought lots of joy and laughter.

The grocery store became busier than normal, and, as a result, I worked extra hours. I loved having the extra hours of work, as it allowed me to earn more to buy gifts for my family.

Eddie and I began investing more and more time together. I really loved being with Eddie. My family really liked him too. He was shy but extremely kind. He also had the most wonderful sense of humor, and we found ourselves laughing often. Honestly, I felt like there was no pretense when I was with him. I was free to be me and vice versa, and he supported my crazy dreams.

Eddie had wonderful family values. He cherished his family, and they were extremely close. He was the middle child of three with an older brother and a younger sister. His parents were funny people too, and I thoroughly enjoyed being around them. I often wondered if Eddie was adopted as he had strawberry blonde hair, blue eyes, and he was really tall. Both of his parents were brunette with brown eyes and average height.

Laughter is a wonderful thing. My dad had this crazy sense of humor and made us all laugh at family meals, but no one had a greater sense of humor than my brother Braden. He made me laugh so hard my cheeks would hurt. I loved how Braden made my mom laugh too. My mom was a smoker, so when Braden got her into a laughing mode, she ended up coughing so hard that she would choke. Mom would ask Braden to stop being so funny as she would become bent over, holding her tummy as it hurt so much to laugh so hard.

By focusing on the great things in my life, I found myself feeling a greater sense of appreciation for my family too.

I believe they felt it, even though we didn't talk about it, and they had no idea what I was writing in the journals that I carried around with me.

Being the youngest of four children came with many benefits. I had two older brothers to look up to and a sister, close in age, to share clothes with. Brandy and I were not especially close as sisters, but we did enjoy sharing our clothes every once in a while.

One of the things that I became fixated on was my goal of being a wildly successful author. I fell in love with this goal. Following Savy's wisdom, I focused on seeing myself be the success that I dreamed of. I connected emotionally to the outcome. I genuinely felt the feelings of being a success. My faith strengthened as I dedicated time every day to feel as if my life was already the success that I desired.

The funny thing is, even though having better grades was not my original intention, the positive aspect, or ripple effect, is that my positive attitude flowed over into other areas of my life, like my grades.

In addition to creating a fun, celebratory home for the holidays, my parents always made a big deal out of our birthdays. Even though my birthday was in December and so close to Christmas, it didn't stop them from making my day a special one. This year my mom planned a family birthday celebration with my entire family, brothers, their spouses, nieces, nephews, my sister, her boyfriend Steve, and my boyfriend, Eddie.

The nineteenth rolled around, and Mom put up HAPPY BIRTHDAY banners, placed balloons around the house, and baked me my favorite carrot cake with cream cheese icing. Everyone was scheduled to arrive at 6 p.m.

By 6:15 p.m. that evening, the house was buzzing with excitement. In some ways, it felt like a pre-Christmas celebration, but everyone came together to celebrate me.

An hour had passed, and my brother Braden had not yet arrived. I asked his wife, Lucie, where she thought he was, and she told me that he installed a new stereo in his car the night before and went for a drive before coming to Mom and Dad's. He drove a Ford Galaxy 500, and he babied his car. He told her that he would meet her there.

Did he get distracted with time? Did he forget where Mom and Dad lived? Obviously, he knew exactly where Mom and Dad lived as we had lived in the same home for my first eight years until he moved out. But where was he?

My mom was a bit of a worrier. I could tell by the look on her face that she was concerned and getting more and more anxious as the minutes passed.

At 7:25 p.m., the doorbell rang. I found it odd that Braden would ring the doorbell when he typically would walk right in. Mom went to the door first, with my dad trailing behind her.

A local policeman from town, fully dressed in uniform, stood at the door. Our family was familiar with this officer because Braden had previously had some run-ins with the law. Braden was a reckless teenager and didn't always make the best decisions. Fortunately, he never went to prison, but he had some close brushes with arrests.

Constable Buchannan began to speak to my mom and dad. There was a lot of noise in the house, and I couldn't hear what he was saying to my parents, but within a couple of minutes, I saw my mom collapse to the floor. My dad stood there in shock. Everyone became quiet. Lucie, Braden's wife, ran to be beside them to find out what was going on.

The Policeman informed us that Braden was in a horrible accident. He was driving in a neighboring town, and his car was hit by an ambulance in full-speed mode heading to the hospital with a patient in the back.

Braden must have been listening to his new stereo and didn't hear the sirens of the ambulance. He entered an intersection with a green light but didn't notice an ambulance heading straight for him. He was hit broadside.

Braden was still alive but hanging on for dear life. He was in the Intensive Care Unit of the local hospital, and they said the prognosis wasn't good. The ambulance he collided with flipped over on impact, and the patient died on the scene. The ambulance attendants were badly shaken but were not in serious condition.

When Lucie grasped the gravity of the situation, she became hysterical. Braden and Lucie's two children were confused. They were two years old and four years old at the time; Billy was the older child, and Amanda was the toddler.

My sister, Brandy, jumped in and took charge. She offered to watch all four of the kids while everyone raced down to the hospital. I decided to drive because my parents and Lucie were badly shaken.

Within minutes, Mom, Dad, Braden's wife Lucie, my brother Clancy, Clancy's wife Allison, Eddie, and I were at the emergency section of the hospital. During the drive to the hospital, I kept silently repeating to myself that Braden would be alright.

A hospital employee greeted us and informed us that Braden was in surgery and asked the entire group to follow her to a nearby waiting room. She opened the door to a private waiting room and suggested we wait there until the doctor could give us an update.

We didn't have any more information, other than he was in critical condition, and they didn't know if he was going to make it.

Minutes turned into hours. My mom was an absolute wreck. She would go from fits of crying to holding her head and rocking back and forth. I would attempt to calm her down, but she was in a heap of emotional pain. Every once in a while, she would get really quiet and then go back to despondency.

My brother Clancy called home to check in on the kids. Brandy reported the kids had all fallen asleep. Her boyfriend Steve had stayed to keep her company while she waited for the update on Braden.

Clancy and Allison also had two children. Their oldest, Lilly, was three years old and their baby, Ralph, was one. Brandy had a way with kids and often babysat for both brothers. She played games, and we called her the pied piper because she had this unique ability to bring order to, what could be, a chaotic environment.

Minutes later, a doctor in green scrubs walked into the waiting room. Instantly I could tell he did not have good news. His face was serious, and he looked exhausted.

"I'm Doctor McPhee, and I performed the surgery on Braden. I am deeply sorry to report that Braden has taken a turn for the worse and, because of the accident and his head injuries, his brain is swollen, and there is no brain activity whatsoever. We are keeping him alive with machines, but he only has a matter of hours."

We all stood there, stunned.

"Before I go, I would like to bring something to your attention. When doing the surgery and the scans, and in our attempt to release the pressure, we discovered Braden had a massive tumor on his brain. Had he been diagnosed with this? Do any of you know anything about that?"

Lucie answered in between her sobs. "I cannot believe this is happening. How could this have happened? This must be a bad dream, and I am going to wake up. Nothing can be done? Nothing at all? I simply can't believe this. And, no, he had not been diagnosed, but he had been experiencing massive headaches the last few months, but he never got it checked out. He was becoming absent-minded and would forget things. He would be in the middle of a sentence and stop talking. And, on top of all of this, he had a brain tumor?"

Dr. McPhee went on, looking at all of us. "Based on what we determined, he very likely only had a matter of months to live as this tumor was massive, aggressive, and positioned in a way that surgery would not have been an option."

This news was completely shocking. My mom began to wail. I have never heard anyone cry like that before. Her pain and distress distracted me from my own. My dad also began to sob; in all my years, my dad never cried in front of us kids until now.

Lucie, in the same state as my mom, was devastated. She cried uncontrollably. I stood in the middle of this waiting room, trying to figure out who to console first. I was actively concerned about the others; I had not personally processed the devastating news.

Braden and I were the closest of the four kids. For some reason, we just clicked, and we were very close despite the eight-year age difference. We could talk about anything, and he was my biggest confidant. Braden was also driven to succeed, and he felt life had something bigger in store for him. He pursued his dreams and wasn't allowing anything or anyone to stand in his way. Sometimes there were moments, since meeting Savy, that I felt Braden somehow knew some of the wisdom Savy had taught.

Braden left the family home when I was eight years old, but he never lost touch with me, even though he stopped talking to my parents for an entire year. Braden and I had regular rendezvous where we met at the local coffee shop and talked about the exciting things in our lives. When Chad broke up with me, Braden was the first person I called.

Dr. McPhee offered the family the opportunity to be with Braden until they removed the life support machines. He knew he had a difficult question to ask, but he felt he needed to ask: "Does anyone know if Braden agreed to donate his organs?"

Lucie spoke first, "Yes, he is definitely an organ donor. He was a huge supporter and often encouraged others to sign their organ donor card on their driver's license."

"Thank you," replied Dr. McPhee. "I will pass this information along to the other medical staff and the organ donor team of physicians. My sincere condolences to all of you. You can go and be with Braden now, and we will be taking him for surgery in approximately two hours."

This entire day was surreal. And then it hit me: Braden was dying on my birthday. I felt a surge of goosebumps come over my entire body.

Braden was dying. I would never see him or talk with him again. An overwhelming feeling of sadness consumed me, and I burst into tears.

Chapter 8

The next few days were a complete blur. My parents were completely distraught. Between Brandy, Clancy, and me, we organized the entire funeral for the 23rd of December. At a time when most people were celebrating the holidays, we were all consumed in grief, and our worlds felt completely torn apart.

The funeral was a magnificent celebration of Braden's life. Braden was so loved and had many friends. The church was packed full to the rafters. There was standing room only, and people lined up in the aisles and out the back door.

The minister and all of the speakers honoring Braden did a fabulous job. Braden's best friend Sonny delivered the eulogy that had the entire congregation laughing and crying. Sonny's real name was Dave, but when Braden and Sonny were young, Braden gave him the nickname Sonny because of his happy-go-lucky demeanor. Braden's children Billy and Amanda attended, but they were too young to really understand what was going on. Lucie did her utmost best to keep her composure for the children. I was impressed with her strength, but I know deep down inside she was dealing with his passing in her own way.

My mom and dad were not keeping it together. My mom barely spoke after Braden died, and she cried often. My dad became a recluse. He kept to himself and didn't want to talk about anything. No parent should ever have to bury their child, and as much as I attempted to bring some cheer to my parent's life, they told me that I simply didn't understand.

They were right. I couldn't have imagined how painful that was for them. I was dealing with my own kind of pain, as Braden and I were so close, but the pain our parents felt must have been significantly worse.

Our own Christmas celebration became unimportant. We maintained the celebration on Christmas Eve and Christmas Day as planned with the entire family for the benefit of the children, but it was a sullen event.

Two days after Christmas, a condolence card arrived in the mail for me. I didn't recognize the handwriting, and it didn't have a return mailing address; however, when I opened it, I discovered Savy sent it.

Immediately I began to wonder how he got my address. How did he know my last name? How did he know my brother died? It dawned on me that the media covered the accident and the funeral extensively. The local news station interviewed me to get more of the details from a family member. I suppose Savy saw that segment on the news. Living in a small town created a clear communication channel as well, and there were very few secrets in Bridlewood.

This is Savy's letter in its entirety:

Dear Sophie,

I heard about the passing of your brother Braden. My sincere condolences to you and your family.

Understand that in this Universe, nothing is ever created or destroyed. Braden's soul will go on to the next phase of his eternal journey. He's no longer in his physical form, but he's very much still alive.

The Bible tells you to call on the spirits, and they will be there. When Braden came into this world, he made a transition from spirit to form. Now Braden has made a transition again. This time from form to spirit. Energy returns to its source of origination. Don't hold on to Braden. If you mentally go back to when Braden was around, you were full of joy. Let him be free and be joyous that he is out of all pain. He is going home. Hold only good thoughts of Braden. Harvest all the good that he brought to your lives while his physical presence was here. He takes all of that with him, and you get to keep it as well. Love Braden and release his soul. God bless you and your family.

On an unrelated note, my apologies but it is necessary to cancel our meeting on the first of January. As it turns out, I had surgery a week ago and received a new heart. Yes, you read that right, I had a heart transplant. I was born with a congenital heart defect and had open-heart surgery when I was a baby. The surgery solved the issue for a time period, but as I aged, my heart became worn and deteriorated to a point where the only option was a heart transplant.

I promise to reach out to you when I am ready to resume our rendezvous in the park. Until then, stay focused, stay strong, and keep moving forward with positive expectations.

Love and gratitude to you and for you,

P.S. If you feel the urge to call me anytime, please use my private and personal telephone number pasted immediately below.

I was grateful to receive Savy's letter and his kind words. It was impressive that he took the time to write a letter when he had just gone through a major operation. I can only imagine how difficult the recovery would be. I found myself feeling genuine concern for Savy's health.

Savy's words about Braden's passing really touched my heart. He had a unique approach to death. I never thought about death in this way. It certainly was a fascinating understanding of energy and transition and spirits and all that stuff.

All of a sudden, it dawned on me, and I felt head-to-toe goosebumps.

"Wait a minute! He had a heart transplant . . . a heart transplant?"

Part II

Chapter 9

Months passed, and I didn't hear a word from Savy. I began to wonder if he was okay. Maybe the heart transplant wasn't as successful as they hoped. I had to shift my thoughts to focus on the positive. This became a way of life for me—think a negative thought, switch to positive. Savy would have recommended that I do.

My parents were seeing a therapist to deal with the grief of my brother's passing. I believe it helped them to some degree. I also believe that time was going to be a helpful healer. For me, I harnessed Savy's wisdom yet again and chose to cherish the fond memories of Braden. In the months that followed Braden's passing, I saw him in my dreams, and in some strange way, it felt like we were still connected.

My sister and I graduated from high school. Brandy chose to go to university and signed up for the business program at Tullus University, located within an hour's drive from our home. Since she graduated as a top honor student, she received a full scholarship to Tullus. She was very grateful for the scholarship as she wasn't sure how she would pay for the tuition, books, and other expenses related to going to university. I think my parents were relieved too.

Following high school, I managed to secure a full-time job at the same town hall where my father worked. Dad helped me get in. I was a cashier in the tax department. Every three months, the taxes were due. Some of the local residents came in to pay their taxes, and I was the one who greeted them and processed their tax payments. I also processed the payments received by mail. I loved the work, but mostly I loved the people. I developed friendships with my co-workers, and we socialized together outside of office hours.

Eddie and I were still going strong. Our love developed into a strong bond, and we got along beautifully. We didn't talk about our next steps, but I suspect we were both thinking about our future. Eddie worked full time with his father, who ran a construction company. He also loved his work, and his father was grooming him to take over the business one day. My inner knowing told me that we were going to be together forever.

I kept the letter Savy sent to me and looked at it daily. One day, as I was studying his letter, my eyes glanced down to his personal and private telephone number. I never called him, although I thought about it from time to time.

Several months had passed since I saw Savy, and I decided it was time to call. I grabbed the phone and dialed his number.

"Hello," answered Savy after several rings. "How may I serve?"

The exuberant manner in which he answered the phone surprised me. I wondered who answers their phone with a question like that.

"Hi Savy, it's Sophie. How are you?" I asked with genuine concern.

"Oh, hi, Sophie! What a pleasant surprise to hear from you," Savy replied with enthusiasm. "I am wonderful, which means, filled with wonder. How about you?"

I chuckled at his response. "Doing great, Savy. It is so good to hear your voice. Thank you for the letter you sent after my brother Braden passed. And, thank you for telling me about your heart transplant as well. That is a major operation. How are you feeling now?"

"Feeling on top of the world. Never better. In fact, life gets better and better every day in every way. What are you doing these days? Did you graduate from school? Are you working now?" Savy asked.

Savy sounded fabulous. I loved his enthusiasm. I had almost forgotten about the authority he had when he spoke. I had a feeling that if Savy spoke, people listened. I certainly did.

"Savy, not only did I graduate from high school, but I even managed to lock in some high grades, As and Bs. It was a great finish. Eddie and I went to the prom together and had the best time ever. I secured a job at the Town Hall, and I love my work."

"What about your writing? Where are you with that? What progress have you made?" Savy asked without commenting on my grades, Eddie, or my new job.

"Wow, you remembered! Thank you."

"Of course, I remembered. It's your passion. This is what you told me you wanted to do with your life," Savy said.

"Other than focusing on the feeling state of being a world-famous author, I haven't done anything else." As the words came out of my mouth, I realized in that moment how ridiculous that seemed.

"Sophie, I know we aren't sitting on our special park bench, but let me offer you some guidance. Write! For goodness sakes, write! Start writing! Authors write. It isn't enough to dream about your ideal life. You have to take action. There is a saying that I heard years ago, and it goes like this: faith without work is dead."

Savy had a way of being stern and loving at the same time.

"I know, I know. I had a feeling you were going to say that," I responded sheepishly.

"Listen, Sophie, I am heading into a meeting in a few minutes, but here's what I would suggest that you do next. Sit down and determine when you intend on completing your first draft of your book. Set a date for completion. Work expands to the time allotted. Decide if you want to self-publish your book or secure a publisher. Either way, answer that question based on what you would love. And, let's meet in a couple of weeks at our favorite meeting place, nice and early in the morning if the time works for you. Say 6:30 a.m.? On the 21st?"

"Works beautifully, Savy. 6:30 a.m. is absolutely perfect. I start work at 8:30 now, so this will give me plenty of time to get to work on time."

We exchanged our goodbyes and hung up the phone.

Chapter 10

Three days had passed since I spoke with Savy. His advice was threefold: set a date for completion, start writing, and decide if I wanted to self-publish or secure a publisher. I hadn't done any of these three things yet. I decided it was time to move into action.

After a wonderful, productive day at work, it was clear to me that tonight was the night for me to follow through. My parents were visiting Lucie and the kids, Brandy was at her boyfriend's house for the evening, and I had the house all to myself.

Seated comfortably at the kitchen table, with my pen and paper and agenda, I began my assignment.

First things first, determine the date I would love to have the first draft of my book completed. I reviewed my calendar, and other than work, my agenda was wide open. Eddie and his father were working day and night on a construction project, and he informed me that he would be tied up for the next week. My weekend and evenings were free.

The date for completing my first draft was going to be in ten days. The thought of writing a book in ten days seemed absurd, especially when I had never written a book before. I decided to stretch myself and go for it; after all, Savy had told me when I set a goal, I should not be concerned about the *how*. Since I was meeting with Savy in ten days, I wanted to surprise him and bring him a copy of my first draft, so ten days felt like a winner.

Even though I had never written a book before, I had read hundreds of books and felt it couldn't be that complicated to write one. This was the belief that I chose to hang onto.

In English class at school, I had written a few short stories and received high marks; therefore, I felt confident I could write. Plus, the idea for the book had been percolating in my mind for about a year. It was simply a matter of sitting down and getting to work.

The discipline that I incorporated was the following: I got up at 5:30 a.m. and wrote for a couple of hours, then went to work. In the evening, I reviewed what I had written that morning.

Surprisingly, my first draft was completed in just nine days. It flowed out of me like water rolling downhill. It was much easier than I anticipated. I printed the rough draft, reviewed it, and stuffed it into my backpack to show Savy.

At 6:25 a.m. on the 21st, I was comfortably seated on the park bench awaiting Savy's arrival. Promptly at 6:29 a.m., Savy rounded the corner and headed in my direction.

Savy had his arms outstretched for a hug. We had never hugged before, and it was such a warm and wonderful way to greet.

"Savy, it is wonderful to see you again! It has been a long time. And, may I add, you look wonderful."

"Thank you, my friend," he said with genuine kindness. "I feel wonderful. How are you doing these days, Sophie? And, did you follow through with my recommendations from our last conversation?"

"Sure did, Savy," I said with pride. "Want to see something?"

"Of course," he responded.

I reached into my backpack and pulled out the draft of my book and handed it to him.

"What's this, Sophie? Did you finish your book? Already?" He seemed to be surprised.

"Yes, the first draft is written. I set a completion date for today, and I got on with the work. I disciplined myself to write every single day, and I found that once I got into the spirit of writing, it flowed with ease." I answered him while grinning from ear to ear. I felt like a proud kid showing off a perfect grade on a test.

"How does it feel to have accomplished this task?" Savy asked.

"Savy, I have to be honest with you. When I decided to write this first draft in ten days, I truly didn't think it could be done, but I felt there was no harm in trying, and you did tell me not to worry about the *how*. I also found that my thoughts were not really supportive of my dream. I could hear this inner voice saying things like, 'Who do you think you are?' and 'You can't write' and 'Who would want to read anything you wrote?' I realized those types of thoughts were not going to help me get it done, so I became the observer of these thoughts and quietened that voice and just stayed laser-focused on getting it done."

"Sophie, you were experiencing your old paradigms. They were attempting to hold you back. That's what paradigms do when you stretch yourself and pursue your dreams."

"When those old beliefs reveal their ugly heads, how do you suggest I handle them?"

Savy responded without skipping a beat. "You replace them. The best way to create a new paradigm, in other words, is to build the belief system within you to support your dreams and to get into a routine of repetition of impressing new paradigms into your subconscious mind. There are two known ways to change a paradigm. The first is through an *emotional impact* and the second way is with *spaced time repetition* of a new belief.

"Sophie, you created your SABY journal. I remember you telling me about this. Your SABY journal included your scripts and beliefs to support your dreams. Here's what I would suggest. Put all of your scripts into one document and then make a recording of your script. This is a powerful exercise. I call this a *power life script*. Ensure that your script is created with positive words only and written in the present tense. The idea behind reinforcing these new ideas into your consciousness through repetition is to feel as if your goal and dreams have already materialized. When your power life script is written properly, you will see, in your mind's eye, the evidence of your amazing life. By doing this and listening to your recording every day, you feel as if you are living that life, and when you do, you are in harmony with your goals. You are vibrating in alignment with your desired outcomes. You become one with your goal. You think *from* your goal instead of trying to move *towards* your goal."

"Wow, Savy, this sounds amazing. I think you may have created the perfect recipe for cooking up any goal. I love the simplicity of this." I was genuinely appreciative of Savy sharing this with me.

"The most important part of manifesting is the *feeling* part. You must *feel* as if you already have that which you desire. The power life script is a tool to help accomplish this, but at the end of the day, manifesting isn't about what you are doing—it is all about how you are feeling. *Feeling* is the secret to manifesting. Simple, yes, but not easy. Remember I shared that with you before?"

"I sure do. I've found myself dealing with old paradigms coming up all of the time, but I find that if I follow a three-step process of noticing, deciding, and switching, I can master any negative thought or feeling that arises."

I continued excitedly, "Savy, this is incredibly helpful. Thank you. But as much as I have this dream to be a wildly successful international best-selling author, I honestly don't know how to get there. I remember you told me that I didn't have to know how, but what do I do next? It seems like I figured out the *how* when it comes to writing, but there must be so much more to it than that."

Savy responded with more of his great wisdom.

"It was Martin Luther King Jr. who said that you do not have to see the whole staircase, just take the first step. You have done that Sophie, you took the first step and wrote your rough draft. The next step is going to be dependent upon whether you are going to self-publish your book or publish it. What have you decided?"

"I haven't decided because I don't understand what the benefits or the challenges are to either one," I answered, "However, I am totally open to figuring this out, and I'll do some research to determine my next step."

"Perfect! Doing research is a next step, Sophie," Savy pointed out. "Doing the research will help you figure out the next step and then determine the next step, and so on. You are well on your way, Sophie. Keep up the great effort and always stay connected to your outcome. Live as if you already are the success you desire to be."

"Live as if? Do I spend as if too? I don't think I really understand the concept of living as if. Would you please elaborate for me?"

"Happy to. When you are living *as if*, you are not necessarily out spending money you don't have; however, you are imagining that you are already living this life. This is happening in your imagination. Your imagination is one of your mental faculties and a resource to put you into the vibratory rate to attract to you everything required for the fulfillment of your desire. Go to the library or the local bookstore and learn everything you can about The Law of Vibration. This is also why you don't need to know the HOW. The way will be revealed to you once you step into the vibratory flow. Allow the Universe to guide you. Listen to your intuition as well. Your intuition is another mental faculty that you have. Everyone has intuition, but some have developed it more than others. Does all of this make sense to you?" Savy asked.

"It's perfect. You are perfect. I love this. You have been, once again, incredibly helpful. Thank you so very much. It's time to get to work, Savy, so I better run."

I honestly didn't want to leave. I would have loved to spend hours or even days with Savy. Being around him made me feel like I could do anything. He definitely brought out the best in me. I felt an overwhelming sense of gratitude.

"Sophie, you have my telephone number. Reach out to me when you want to meet again. I am happy to meet with you anytime. I love that you are devoted to your dreams. Your actions will inspire others to pursue theirs. I suspect you are already positively impacting those around you with your action taking, positive attitude, and new disciplines. Let your light shine, and you will inspire others to do the same. That's one of the marvelous ripple effects of following your dreams."

"Thank you, Savy. You are very kind. I will definitely call you. Thank you again. *Ciao* for now," I responded as I got up to walk away.

"Sophie, just one second. Thank you for printing and bringing me the draft of your book. I look forward to reading it. Would you please provide me with your telephone number as well?"

"Of course. I wrote it on the front page of the draft, just in case you wanted it."

"Oh, I didn't notice it was there—that's perfect," Savy said. "Thank you. Have a wonderful day."

"You too, Savy. Talk with you soon." I said as I began to head back home.

Chapter 11

Several more months had passed, and my research was complete. After studying options for first-time authors, I decided to pursue a publisher. My next step was to secure a literary agent. Apparently, in order to get an agent, it is essential to have the book written and have a completed book proposal.

A book proposal is a detailed document that provides the content of the book or a sample chapter, marketing plan, publicity strategy, comparisons to other books on the market, and the author's credentials; all essentially designed to prove the salability of the book. The proposal would also show a publisher that the author clearly understands that they are committed to market their book.

During my research, I found an article written by a famous author who claimed that 5 percent of an author's responsibility is completing the book, and 95 percent of the author's responsibility is marketing it. That finding surprised me, but after digging more, I discovered it appeared to be true. Knowing that I would have one chance to make a first impression, I devoted the necessary time to create the most amazing book proposal ever.

It sounded easy enough; however, I found it to be more work than the writing of the book itself. The hours put into this proposal boggled my mind. Gratefully, after a couple of months, I completed the proposal and was ready to send out query letters to potential literary agents.

The act of preparing a proposal definitely became beneficial. It helped me understand an industry that I previously was unfamiliar with, and it helped me recognize what I needed to do, as the author, to create success for my book. Writing a proposal allowed me to consider other books on the market and to comprehend and communicate how mine was different from any other book out there.

In my proposal, I compared my book to many of the classics that had gone on to sell millions of copies. My book would be the next great classic. I didn't hope it would; I knew it would. I also understood the difference between hoping, wishing, and believing. A total unwavering belief was the emotion required to create the desired results. It is a feeling of certainty, a knowing that your desire is already done; Savy had graced my awareness with that.

My book was written in a parable style, which is a fiction book with valuable lessons for the reader. I personally loved the parable type of book and read many of them over the years.

After Savy suggested I write a power life script, I did follow through and created a detailed description of my amazing life, written with only positive present-tense words, connecting vividly to my senses, seeing the end result as if it was already in my life now. And since I recorded my script, I dedicated time every day to listen to it. I felt myself emotionally getting stronger and stronger every day.

Little did Eddie know, but I had scripted in my power life script that we were happily married, and we had a lovely family. I saw us living in a beautiful home that we owned outright. I also saw myself enjoying the benefits of being a successful author. I wrote about seeing my books on the bestseller lists, and I saw myself walking into bookstores and seeing my book on the front shelves at the entranceway where they kept all of the big bestsellers.

In my imagination, I was also doing national media interviews and having a great time. The press and the reviews raved about my book, and it had reached what they call "the tipping point," and it was selling in droves. I saw the foreign rights translations for the book and actively felt gratitude for the abundance of royalty funds arriving. In my mind, I would see Eddie and me celebrating by taking elaborate trips and buying exotic cars. Eddie was a car buff and loved antique cars, and because I loved him so, I wanted him to be happy and have everything he wanted.

I also saw myself helping Lucie out with the kids. Since Braden had passed, she was struggling to make ends meet. Braden didn't have any life insurance, and Lucie was previously a stay-at-home mom. Lucie had to secure a job to maintain some kind of normalcy so that they, as a family, could remain in their family home. My parents didn't have a lot of money, but I know they were helping her out as much as they could. My mom would prepare meals for Lucie and the kids and take them over to her.

One of the things that I intended to do, once I was successful as an author, was to pay for Lucie's home and give her some money that could be a cushion for her to use as she wished.

My power life script was very detailed and included every area of my life, from my career to my relationships, friendships, home, finances, gifts, and donations.

I would listen to my recorded version of my power life script every day. It was a thirty-minute walk to work. I loved getting outside, enjoying fresh air, and so, with my headphones on, my power life script played in my ears and filled me automatically with that *it's already done* feeling. I smiled all the way to work and all the way back home. After all, who wouldn't smile living a life like the one that I had designed!

Upon identifying thirty-seven potential literary agents, I mailed out individualized, personalized query letters to them all, offering to send my detailed proposal, should they be interested in representing me and my book. My query letter was well written and displayed confidence. I expected to hear back from all of them.

The letters were sent, and I patiently waited. Patience had not been my strong point, but I expected it might take a bit of time.

After several more months passed, I became frustrated and a bit angry. After all, how could these literary agents not be jumping at the chance to represent the author of the next great classic?

In my emotional state of frustration, I decided to call Savy and schedule another meeting. We set to meet in a couple of days, and I had several questions ready for him.

The day of our meeting arrived. This time I made a thermos of coffee and brought two cups and freshly home-made blueberry muffins I had made the night before. It was going to be a bit more enjoyable on this cool day to have the coffee and muffins during our meeting.

Savy and I both arrived at the exact same time. We hugged, said our usual greetings, and sat down on our bench.

"Sophie, you brought coffee and muffins? How kind of you. Thank you. This is a lovely surprise."

"It's starting to get cooler in the mornings, and I felt a warm thermos of coffee would keep us warm inside. The blueberry muffins are home-made— I baked them last night—almost fresh out of the oven." I extended my hand to offer Savy one.

I continued as I wanted to get straight to business. It was time to ask Savy some questions about Savy.

"Savy, I don't know anything about you. We are always talking about me, my family, my dreams, my life, but what about you?"

"My life is rather simple, really. I am a businessman. I am happily married to the woman of my dreams and have been for forty-seven years now. I am blessed with three wonderful children and ten amazing grandchildren. Sophie, I appreciate the interest, but I am here to serve you. How may I serve?"

There is that question again! *How may I serve?* I heard him answer the telephone with that question the first time I called him. We didn't have a lot of time together this morning, and I had several questions and decided to get to them.

"Savy, I worked for months on an amazing book proposal to prepare to sell my book to a publisher," I began.

"Okay, it sounds like you decided to secure a publisher rather than self-publish your book," he commented.

"Yes, that's right. I considered the options, and, in my research, I learned about the challenges and benefits to both. I determined that I would rather have my book published by a publishing house, but not just any publishing house, but one of the big ones.

"Therefore, I created a solid book proposal, researched the best literary agents in the business, and sent out personalized query letters to thirty-seven of them. I sent these letters more than two months ago, and I haven't heard a thing. Not a peep. Not one response whatsoever. I started to wonder if they got lost in the mail, but thirty-seven of them? I don't think so.

"Now, I find myself frustrated. I don't know what to do next. Write them again? What do you suggest, Savy?"

Savy immediately responded without hesitation. "Many years ago, I heard the phrase '*wait as the one who understands*' which means, when you know your goal has already manifested in your mind, you have infinite patience. Infinite patience produces immediate results. Just think about that for a moment, Sophie."

"I think I get it," I responded with a bit of hesitation.

"You still have options, Sophie," Savy declared.

"Sophie, you have the option to self-publish your book, bring it out to the world, demonstrate that people will love it, and allow a publisher to find you. There are many roads to get you to where you want to go. Do not assume that you have to figure it all out. Remember what I shared with you at one of our earlier meetings? You do not have to know HOW. Stay connected to the outcome as if it is already done, and you will attract to you everything required for the fulfillment of the desire. You must have faith.

"My advice to you, Sophie, is to prepare for success. Are you living as if you expect to succeed as an author, or are you living in a state of hope or wish? Belief is essential for success. If you don't believe it now, you'll never see it. You must first believe, and then you'll see; not the other way around." Savy shared these words with total confidence.

"I get it, Savy. Thank you. So what can I do to prepare for success as a best-selling author?"

"Easy! Create a mock-up of your book cover and paste a best-seller emblem on the cover and visualize seeing your book as a best-seller. Create a shelf in your home where you'll display your best-selling books and the copies of the many languages they have been translated into. Design a mock-up version of the best-seller list showing your book as the number one best-seller. Create visuals that allow you to feel the end result. In your mind, see yourself going to the bank with the royalty payment and handing it to the teller and see her expression of shock when she sees the large amount written on the check. Visualize multiple payments made out to you, arriving in the mail for all of the royalties you have earned from the millions of books sold. Become one with the outcome you desire. Know it to be true. Feel it. Feel it genuinely in your soul. Feel it as if you were born for this.

"The most powerful thing you can do, Sophie, is to focus on your end result prior to going to sleep every night. Those pre-sleep moments, just before you drift off into sleep, are the most powerful moments of the day. Because you are in a relaxed state at that time, what you are thinking about and feeling will determine what shows up in your life most of the time. I would suggest that you write out this question and put it directly beside your bed: NOW THAT MY DREAM IS FULFILLED, HOW DO I FEEL? And when you see the result of that question in your imagination, connect to it and drift off into sleep, knowing it is already done. Do this, and I guarantee you, you will manifest your desires. It works every time, not once in a while, every time."

"Okay, Savy, I am on it!" I responded with conviction. "This is going to intensify the feelings. Thank you. I am so grateful for you. You are a blessing in my life."

"Sophie, you have my number. Call me with an update, please," Savy expectantly and joyfully demanded as he got up to leave.

"I promise I will, Savy. Talk with you soon, and have a great day!"

"You too, Sophie, and thank you for the coffee and the blueberry muffins. They were delicious."

Chapter 12

Two days after meeting Savy in the park, a letter arrived from a literary agent from the west coast. His name was Timothy Bailor, and he was an independent literary agent. He was essentially a one-man show.

Timothy's letter requested that I send the full proposal, including the entire manuscript. He said he would evaluate it and promised to get back to me within days of receipt. The tone of his letter was warm and complimentary. It sounded promising to me, and if he really liked the book and the proposal, maybe I have secured myself an agent.

The very next morning, I couriered the contents of the package to Timothy. I could have sent it in the mail, but I wanted it to get there faster so he could dive right in.

I felt giddy inside, waiting for a response. In some ways, it felt like Christmas as I always expected Santa (aka my parents) to bring wonderful surprises, and of course, Santa never disappointed.

A few days after I sent the package to Timothy, I received a telephone call at work. I asked Timothy to make it quick as I was only on a short break. Timothy got right down to business. He said that he loved my book and the proposal and definitely wanted to represent me as my literary agent.

He offered to call back to review the contents of a literary agent and author contract. I asked him to call that evening at 7 p.m., and at 6:59 p.m., my telephone rang. Like Savy, Timothy was prompt!

It was great to hear his voice. He spoke softly, so much so I could hardly hear him. He also sounded very young. I felt it might have been rude to ask him for his age. He raved about my book and the proposal and felt strongly he could secure a publishing deal. The details of the literary agent contract sounded pretty standard to me. I had already done my research and understood a typical contract. I agreed to all conditions, and he said he'd courier the contract to me in the morning.

I wanted to call Savy right away to tell him but decided to try Eddie first. Eddie was out on a job site but promised to call me back later that evening.

Securing a literary agent felt like a huge step in the right direction. It was now Timothy's responsibility to go out and secure a publisher. He did tell me that there was a chance some publishers may ask to meet with me. He suggested for me to be prepared to do some potential traveling. I was ready for anything. This was my dream, and I would do whatever it took to be successful, as long as it was legal, ethical, and moral.

Now it was a matter of waiting for a call from my agent to give me the exciting news that he found a publisher.

Time passed, and there was no word from Timothy. I really didn't have any clue as far as how long it takes to secure a publisher. In my world, I would have loved it to happen within a couple of weeks of signing the literary contract, but that wasn't the case. Weeks passed, and the weeks turned into months. Patience was no longer my best virtue, and I was getting impatient.

I reflected back to a conversation I had in my early dialogues with Savy when he said, 'pray and move your feet.' Maybe it was time for me to move my feet. I had certainly been doing lots of praying.

In the meantime, Eddie and I were at a point where we had begun discussions about our future plans. Both of us were shy at first to bring it up, but once the ice was broken, we couldn't stop talking about our future plans. We wanted to be together every day and every night. We talked about the type of home we would love to live in and designed it in our minds. It was premature, but we even discussed having children and the many fun activities we would do with our kids.

As Valentine's Day approached, I was starting to wonder if Eddie was going to pop the question. Knowing Eddie and his unromantic style, I didn't think he would use such a conspicuous holiday to ask me to marry him . . . or would he?

One week before Valentine's Day, Eddie called me to tell me that he wanted this Valentine's Day to be special. He made a reservation at my favorite Italian restaurant and asked me to be ready for 6 p.m. when he would pick me up.

I loved Italian food, and since my grandmother came from Italy, she cooked authentic Italian food every Sunday and opened her home to her children and grandchildren. I didn't get to Grandma's as often as I would have loved, but we managed to sneak in a few visits here and there.

I loved visiting my grandma, and every time I did, I left her home feeling like I was going to burst from eating so much and from an overwhelming feeling of being loved. Eddie loved her too, especially when she would squeeze his cheeks.

My grandma pulled me aside on one of our more recent visits to tell me she had a premonition that Eddie was going to ask me to marry him. I thought she was being playful, and I said, "Nah, that can't be." She quickly grabbed my face with her two hands and said with her Italian accent, "Marka my words, dear, it will happen within the next six months."

Valentine's Day arrived, and with my new red dress, black high-heeled shoes, hair and make-up done, I was ready for Eddie to take me to dinner.

"Wow, Sophie, you look beautiful tonight," Eddie exclaimed with a nervous voice as he handed me a single red rose. He was dressed in a beautiful baby blue dress shirt with a dark navy jacket. He had beige pants on, and he looked stunning. I was pleasantly taken aback when I saw him, as I honestly could say he had never looked so good. All I could think is that he was mine, all mine.

As the waitress seated us at the table next to the fireplace, I wondered if Eddie had made a special request for this table or if we were just fortunate that evening to get this special spot.

The menus were delivered, we made our choices, and the delicious food arrived. Everything about our meal and the evening was perfect. The wine was divine, the food was mouth-watering, Eddie looking more handsome than ever, and I had never been more grateful for him.

Eddie reached into his jacket pocket and took out a red envelope and handed it to me. I brought a Valentine's Day card for him too and took it out of my purse and handed it to him. He said, "You first!" indicating I should open my card.

I removed the card from the red envelope, and it was a thick heavy-quality linen card with a beautiful heart on the front. There were no words on the outside of the card. I opened the card, and inside was this riddle:

Hi there, My Love,

Now begins a game.

For the effort you put in,

You will be rewarded the same.

Look for a tube of toothpaste

To find the first clue;

You will soon find out

Where I'm waiting for you.

At first, I wasn't sure what to make of this card. Is this a joke? I honestly didn't understand. Eddie could see the confused look on my face and decided to jump in.

"My love, you are about to embark on a scavenger hunt. Each clue will lead you to another clue, and at the end, you will find me. Are you willing to play along?" he asked.

"Oh, my goodness! Yes, of course. I was so confused. Could you tell? Now it makes sense. Okay, so I get it. When we go home, I have to find a tube of toothpaste, right?"

"Yes, that is it. You've got it. One clue will lead you to another. Well, you get the gist. You've done scavenger hunts before, right?" Eddie asked.

"Yes, we did one at school several years ago, and I found it to be a lot of fun."

After dinner wrapped up, we got in Eddie's car and headed back to my parents. On the way home, Eddie told me that my parents were aware of the scavenger hunt and approved.

Approved? I found that to be an odd word to use, but I felt grateful they were onboard since I wasn't sure whether I was going to be tearing the house apart.

As soon as I arrived home, with Eddie trailing behind me, I went into the bathroom to find my toothpaste tube. Sure enough, a note was wrapped around the tube and held on with an elastic band. I took the note off, unraveled it, and read the following:

At night when you go to sleep,

Look under this to have a peek.

"Pillow!" I shouted, and Eddie laughed.

I started to think that I might be a master at scavenger hunts. This was fun.

The next stop was my bedroom. I looked under the pillow, and there wasn't anything there. Oops, I guess it wasn't the pillow. I got down on the floor and took a peek under the bed. Other than a couple of dust bunnies, I found another note that said:

Roses are red, and violets are blue;

Call your sister for the next clue.

Brandy was over at Steve's that evening, as Steve's parents were out for the night. Steve, being the gourmet chef that he claimed to be, prepared a magnificent dinner for Brandy.

I raced into the kitchen and dialed Steve's number. For some reason, Eddie had disappeared. He was no longer following me. Steve answered the phone and handed it to Brandy.

Brandy only uttered these words and hung up the phone:

It is a place to plant,

A place to grow;

Dad loves it most,

From that, you'll know.

It's the greenhouse! Grabbing my shoes, I started to head to the backdoor. As I opened the backdoor, I could see twinkly lights on in the greenhouse. The entire walkway from the house to the greenhouse was laced with red rose pedals. I could hear the faint sound of music coming from the greenhouse. For a moment, I felt tingly all over.

There was no doubt in my mind that when I walked through that greenhouse door, Eddie would be waiting for me to ask me to marry him. I already knew what I was going to say.

The moment I opened the door, I could hear the music of Andy Gibb and the song "I Just Want to Be Your Everything." This was our song.

Eddie stood there with a big, beautiful bouquet of red roses. He walked toward me. I started to tremble. There was no doubt in my mind I wanted to live the rest of my life with Eddie. The love between us was impenetrable.

Eddie dropped to one knee, held out his hand with a black velvet box opened to reveal a stunning one-carat diamond ring, and said these magical words: "Sophie, would you do me the honor of being my wife?"

"Oh Eddie, yes, of course!"

Eddie slipped the ring on my finger. It fit perfectly. I wondered how he knew my ring size, but then it dawned on me. A couple of weeks earlier, he was playing with my jewelry and put my sapphire ring on his baby finger. I thought it was odd at the time and never gave it a second thought. He must have been doing this to gauge the size of my ring finger, and he nailed it.

Chapter 13

Every once in a while, I would hear from my agent Timothy with an update. He claimed to have submitted my manuscript to a dozen publishing houses but heard nothing back. I was really starting to wonder how long it takes to get a book published. The idea of self-publishing was becoming more and more attractive every day.

However, I had a wedding to plan, and, immediately following our engagement, I moved into wedding planning mode.

I chose my sister Brandy to be my maid of honor, and Eddie chose his brother to be his best man. It became clear to both of us to have a more intimate wedding with family and close friends. Gratefully we managed to keep the wedding list to under a hundred guests. We decided not to have any other people in our bridal party. Keep it simple became our philosophy.

After high school ended, my best friend Becca moved out west with Danny. Becca entered medical school, and Danny got a job to support them. They were struggling to make ends meet with Becca's med school bills, and the expense of coming back home for the wedding simply wasn't possible for them at this time.

In some ways, it became a more exciting wedding for my mom because her daughter was getting married. When my brothers Braden and Clancy married, my mom was not really involved in the wedding plans, although I know she wanted to be. Both Lucie and Allison did their best to include Mom, yet the bond between a mother and daughter is a strong one, and both Lucie and Allison had very close relationships with their mothers.

My mom and my sister Brandy went with me for wedding dress shopping. They helped me choose the perfect dress, the wedding venue, the meal for the reception, wedding guest gifts, photographer, disc jockey, and florist. Eddie trusted me and knew whatever choices I made were going to be perfect for him. One of the beneficial traits of Eddie was his easy-going nature.

The wedding was planned for six months after we became engaged. It would be a beautiful August wedding, and we prayed for a sunny, warm day.

Five weeks before the wedding, on my usual walk to work, I began to have pain in my abdomen, and it intensified with every step I took. The pain was dull at first but became increasingly more painful. By the time I arrived at work, I was buckled over, holding my stomach. My supervisor saw me and said that I wasn't looking very well, and I should go home. The only way back home was to walk, and the idea of walking didn't feel appealing to me. I decided to call my mom and ask her to come and get me. Something about this pain caused me concern.

My mom responded immediately and said she would be at my work to pick me up in twenty minutes. She had already arrived at her work and asked her boss if she could leave to take me to the doctor's office. He reluctantly agreed. She really didn't care what he thought because she was determined to get to me as fast as possible.

By the time mom arrived at my work, I was in tears. The pain was intense. I felt fearful.

We arrived at the doctor's office only to discover the office wasn't open yet. They opened in thirty minutes, and we decided to wait. We sat on the floor in the hallway, waiting for the medical staff to arrive. Minute by minute, the pain seemed to be getting worse.

Soon the nurse arrived to open up the waiting room. She took one look at me and told me to go straight into the examining room. Doctor Abdulla arrived a few minutes later and began to evaluate me. He felt he knew what was wrong. He told me that he suspected it was a ruptured ovarian cyst, and I required surgery immediately. He called the hospital, and they sent an ambulance straight away. The ambulance arrived in a few minutes.

I really didn't like people making a fuss over me, so all of this attention felt awkward. When the ambulance attendants arrived, they helped me get up on the gurney as they didn't want me to walk, and they requested that I move as little as possible. Mom told me she would meet me at the hospital.

The next hour was a blur as they got me prepared for surgery. They gave me a sedative to help me relax and deal with the pain. My mom promised to call Eddie and the other family members to let them know what was going on.

Hours later, I woke up in the recovery room. I could hear the noise of the machines, and even though I felt groggy, I could see a nurse walking toward me. She asked me how I was feeling, but I really felt out of it. She said it was the anesthetic, and it would wear off in time. She asked me about my pain, but I wasn't feeling any at that time. She suggested I rest, and she would check in on me in a little while.

"What happened?" I whispered. I still didn't know what had happened to me. Was it an ovarian cyst that ruptured as Dr. Abdulla suspected? Or was it something else? And, what did it mean as far as having children in the future? I had many questions that I wanted to be answered.

The nurse walked back over to my side and informed me that the doctor would be in soon to explain everything. I fell back asleep.

A couple more hours passed, and then I could hear a faint voice calling my name. I opened my eyes, and a gentleman in green scrubs stood over me. He began to speak.

"Hi Sophie, I'm Doctor Williams, and I performed the surgery on you this morning. How are you feeling right now?"

"Hi," I responded weakly. "I'm feeling pain in my abdomen. It hurts."

The doctor stepped away to whisper something to the nurse. The doctor came back to my side again, and the nurse went to get some pain medication that she injected into my intravenous.

Dr. Williams continued. "Sophie, you had an ovarian cyst, which is a fluid-filled sac that forms on or inside an ovary. In some cases, the cyst can break open or rupture. That is precisely what yours did. It ruptured, and you were bleeding internally. Getting to the hospital as fast as you did was the smartest response. It could have been a lot worse if you didn't go to emergency right away. I am glad you did. In some cases, ovarian cysts are cancerous. We will know better after the biopsy, whether yours was or was not cancerous. Because of the extent of your rupture, during surgery, we had to remove one of your ovaries."

The doctor could see my eyes well up with tears. What did this mean as far as having a family in the future? And cancer? Oh my goodness, could this be real? Is this happening right now? It is one month until our wedding. Would Eddie still want to marry me? All of these gloomy thoughts caused me to feel scared, and tears began to spill out of the corner of my eye.

I felt the doctor may have been reading my mind as he continued by saying, "Sophie, you can still have children. Do not be concerned about that. Also, if the cyst was cancerous, we removed it all. Based on what I saw, I don't believe you have anything to be concerned with. Now, it is time to focus on recovery. You will likely be in the hospital for several days as we monitor you and help you deal with the pain, but you should be back to work in about a month."

"A month? A month? I'm getting married in a month," I said. My voice was hoarse, and it was an effort to get the words out. My throat felt really sore. I could hardly talk.

Dr. Williams advised me to save my voice. He told me that my throat was sore because of the tubes they had down my throat during surgery. He asked me to rest comfortably, knowing that all of this was behind me. Minutes later, I fell asleep again. It was probably the dose of morphine that they gave me to reduce the pain.

While I slept, they transferred me to a room. When I woke up, I saw Mom, Dad, and Eddie sitting in chairs at the end of the hospital bed. Seeing Eddie brought me comfort. He observed my eyes opening and jumped up to join me at my side. He leaned down and kissed me on the forehead. I could see the concern in his eyes. I had an intravenous needle in my left arm, heart monitoring equipment hooked up to my chest, oxygen tubes in my nose, and a catheter inserted to catch the urine. It likely looked much worse than it was.

Within hours the medical staff demanded I get up. I could hardly move. The pain was intense even with the pain medication. They removed the catheter and said that it was essential that I got moving on day one. I was stunned at how difficult it was to get up and to move. I asked for more pain medication, but they told me that I was limited to every four hours, and I still had an hour to go.

Day by day, I improved. The doctor informed me that the cyst was definitely not cancerous and that I would be leaving the hospital in two days. He told me to rest and to not return to work for at least a month and to not do any strenuous activities. He said I would likely feel fine by the time the wedding date came. I was delighted to hear that.

On the afternoon before I was scheduled to leave the hospital, I woke up from a nap to discover Savy sitting in my hospital room. At first, I wondered if I was dreaming, but sure enough, he was there.

"Savy, hi! What are you doing here?" I asked with a sleepy voice.

"Hello to you too, Sophie," he said with a chuckle. "I called your parent's home yesterday only to discover you were here. I came as soon as I could."

For the next few minutes, we talked about the experience I had gone through that resulted in the surgery, and I brought him up to date on securing my literary agent, the status of my book, my work, and my engagement to Eddie and all of our wedding plans.

"Savy, I'd really love to have you and your wife at my wedding, but I didn't have your address to invite you. Eddie and I are getting married on August the 6th. Can you join us, please, as it would be an honor to have you there?"

"Sophie, I'd love to; however, we are out of the country for the entire month of August. My apologies. I am sincerely grateful for the invitation, though. Thank you," Savy said with such sincerity.

Savy went on to share what turned out to be an incredibly valuable lesson.

"Sophie, you have become a very focused and disciplined lady. Based on our conversations, I know you are laser-focused on your goals, but where does health fit in to all of this? In other words, do you declare you have a healthy body? Is this a priority in your life? I have seen it with others, and I have experienced it myself. If one isn't also focused on perfect health, they can meet with unexpected challenges like you did.

"Frankly, I had a similar experience when my heart health began to decline. I hadn't been focused on visualizing and knowing my heart was functioning perfectly; and therefore, the lack of attention and focus caused me to require a heart transplant. Fortunately for me, I received a strong heart, and I feel better than I ever felt in my life. Now, my health is a priority. I give thanks for my perfect health, and I focus on getting better and better every day in every way."

Savy's wisdom inspired me to shift my focus, and I made a note to revise my own power life script to include comments and gratitude about my perfect health as well. His sharing reminded me of his heart transplant and how grateful I was that he was feeling better. In a split second, I flashed back to the letter he sent me after Braden passed away, and I felt I had to ask.

"Savy, when did you have your heart transplant?"

"A couple of years ago around Christmas time. Why do you ask?"

"No no no, I want to know exactly what date? What date did you have your heart transplant?" I pressed him.

"I believe it was the evening of the nineteenth of December. Why are you acting strange, Sophie? What is going on?" Savy became curious and wanted to know where I was going with my questioning.

"Savy, that was the day my brother passed away. He donated his organs. Could you be the one who received his heart? Oh my goodness, this is blowing my mind!"

"Nothing happens by accident, Sophie. Perhaps this makes us family now," Savy said with a smile. "I always felt we have a special connection, young lady."

Oddly enough, I felt a strange sense of peace at the thought of Savy having Braden's heart. I felt even closer to him now.

Chapter 14

By the time our wedding day came along, I felt amazingly well. After my surgery, I unintentionally lost some weight, and after a couple of minor alterations, my wedding dress fit perfectly once again.

On the morning of our wedding, my hairdresser arrived at our home to do my, my sister's and my mom's hair. The make-up artist arrived an hour later, completed applying all of our make-up, and all three of us were ready for the photographer to capture the magical day. The house was filled with laughter and joy. The weather was perfection, exactly as we had hoped it would be: sunny, warm, and with a light fresh breeze.

I found myself missing Becca and wished she was here. She called me to let me know she was thinking of me and to send her best wishes to Eddie and me. I promised to share the photos with her when we received them back from the photographer.

My dad looked incredibly handsome in his tux, and I could tell he felt a bit nervous at the thought of walking me down the aisle and giving away his baby girl. Dad always called me his baby girl, even though I was an adult. He gave me that nickname when I was a baby, and it stuck. Being the youngest of four children, it made perfect sense to me.

In all of the excitement, I hadn't given much thought to the obvious fact that Braden wasn't going to be there for the family photos. Lucie and the kids were coming, and Lucie was bringing a date. That felt weird, but we all wanted her to be happy. Her boyfriend seemed to be a great guy, and he was amazing with the children. He played with them often, and we could tell both Billy and Amanda loved him. He also treated Lucie extremely well.

The entire wedding day was perfect and magical. A limousine was hired to bring me, my sister, my mom, and my dad to the chapel. As we were arriving at the chapel, I could see Eddie greeting all of our guests at the entranceway. He looked amazing. I always found Eddie to be handsome, but on this day, he took that word to a whole new level. He had on a dark navy-blue tuxedo, crisp white shirt, and a white tie. His blue eyes looked like the color of the ocean, and his strawberry blonde hair shone. In only a matter of minutes, he would be my husband. That thought gave me warm chills all over.

Everyone cleared away from the door to find their seats and to get ready for the bride to arrive. Mom was escorted to her seat by Eddie's brother, and Brandy was lined up to go down the aisle with Eddie's brother David.

Eddie stood at the front, beside the Pastor, awaiting my arrival. The organist began to play the wedding march, all of our guests stood up, and my dad proudly escorted me down the aisle. I noticed a tripod and a video camera off in a corner and felt a moment of gratitude because everything seemed to be happening so fast, and I was grateful to have it all recorded.

When we were at the altar exchanging our vows, I could hardly believe it was happening. I was marrying my soulmate, and I reflected back to the day on the bench when I contemplated ending my life because of a relationship breakup. It certainly seemed ridiculous in hindsight.

After we said "I do" to each other, we were whisked away for photos at the park and then over to the reception center for the dinner and after-party. The speeches were few, thankfully, but we enjoyed lots of laughter. There was plenty of tinkling of the glasses, either toasting the bride and groom or making an attempt to get the bride and groom to kiss (an old tradition).

We stayed right until the very end. It was so much fun. Lots of dancing, although I definitely began to feel fatigued closer to the end of the evening. We went to the local hotel and fell into bed in a state of exhaustion.

Eddie and I chose to go to a cabin on a lake for our honeymoon. We only wanted to relax, listen to the sound of the loons, enjoy the sunsets, and connect to nature. It was the most blissful time.

By the time we were back, we were ready for our new life together in our new home, but what we weren't ready for was the insane amount of noise coming from the lower level of the duplex we rented.

Eddie and I found a home located within walking distance of my work and relatively close to my parent's home. Eddie knew how much I loved my morning and evening walks, and he wanted to ensure I would be accommodated. He was incredibly sweet that way. Our new home would be the upper level of a duplex, and the owners lived in the lower level with their three young children. We were a bit concerned about the potential noise, but the owners guaranteed it would be perfectly fine. The rent seemed outrageously high too. Since it was a rental, we knew it would only be temporary.

It took less than two weeks to realize we had made a huge mistake with choosing this rental option. We had signed a year lease, so we felt we had to suck it up for another fifty weeks until we could get out of there.

I created a goal card to use as a visualization tool. I carried it with me, and I would look at it often. It clearly stated: I am so happy and grateful to own our beautiful home outright, and we love our home so much.

I became emotionally involved with Eddie and me living in our beautiful four-bedroom, luxurious home. I also adjusted my power life script to reflect owning a beautiful, quality, four-bedroom, three-bathroom home, with a living room, family room, dining room, kitchen, and double-car garage. I saw us being close to a park and nature trails. I imagined our home being beautifully decorated and tastefully furnished. Both Eddie and I began a new home savings account and socked away as much of our take-home pay as we could.

I was finally back to work after being away for six weeks. It was wonderful to see my colleagues again. The people I worked with loved my positive outlook, as well.

Oftentimes I found myself giving guidance to others who were going through struggles. I became the go-to person when family, friends, and co-workers were experiencing challenges. I had been blessed with having this extraordinary man in my life, by the name of Savy, and his wisdom helped me transform my life, and, as a result, I loved sharing these valuable insights with others.

My actions also inspired others into action. Many who came into contact with me observed me working with my journals, inquired about them, and asked me to share more. I gave journals as gifts and included instruction on the most effective ways to implement positive change.

At the lunch break, I overheard a couple of people speaking about a lottery draw that had just been announced the day before. The draw was being offered by the local children's hospital. It was the Bridlewood Children's Hospital Home Lottery. The tickets were $100 each, and the grand prize was a spectacular, beautifully furnished, professionally decorated, four-bedroom, three-bathroom home in a brand new area of town.

I discovered that the home was open for visitors, and tickets could be purchased directly inside the home during the hours of noon to 8 p.m., Monday through Friday. I planned to go to the house that evening to buy my ticket.

From the moment I walked in the door, I felt a connection to this home. It was spectacular. The décor was amazing, and it looked like a show home that could be highlighted in a decorating magazine. I suppose it was a show-home of sorts. I bought a ticket and proceeded to tour the home room by room.

If Eddie and I could win this home, we would be set. I decided to set my sights on us owning and living in this home, and I modified my goal card by adding in the address, and I also modified my power life script. The drawing for the lottery was scheduled to take place in four months on December 7th.

Every day I would visualize living in that home. In my imagination, I was doing the dishes at the kitchen sink, doing laundry in the laundry room. I went to sleep in that home, woke up in that home, all in my imagination.

When I went to visit the home, I would touch the furniture and feel the fabric. I imagined coming home at night and having intimate dinners with Eddie at our kitchen table. I visualized our families being over for special holiday meals and saw the dining room table prepared for a feast.

I determined which room would be our baby's room and which one would be our guest room. On one of my visits to the dream home, I actually jumped in the big roman bathtub that was in the en-suite bathroom attached to the master bedroom, and I imagined having a bubble bath while listening to some soft classical music with candles glowing.

Every single evening prior to going to sleep, I practiced the recommendation Savy offered to me. I connected to the feelings as I answered the question, *Now that my dream is fulfilled, how do I feel?* I felt the gratitude, the love, the joy as I drifted off into a blissful sleep.

December 7th arrived, and an elderly lady from town won the home. I genuinely felt happy for her. Based on what they said in the media, it sounded like she could definitely benefit from the winnings.

Savy and I had been having fairly regular conversations. He continued to offer advice on various areas of my life. I remembered Savy offering guidance on goals one time, and he said to "detach from the way the goal will come to you and stay focused on the goal no matter what." He also suggested to "deny the evidence of the senses." To me, this meant to stay focused on my goal and not to let someone else winning the home distract me.

Savy felt there is always another way. He said there is always a way when one stays committed. I decided to modify my goal card and my power life script, remove the specific address, and focus on owning a home.

Denying the evidence of the senses meant to live as if we already owned our beautiful home, regardless of living in the upper level of a duplex with massive amounts of noise coming from downstairs.

He highly recommended for us to stay away from any negative emotions, to stop looking at our savings account balance and getting emotionally involved with not having enough. He advised that negativity, even if it is a little, can kill dreams.

Savy had also advised me that goals take time to manifest. He said that the challenge most people have is that they don't know how long a goal will take.

"You have to trust that it will take whatever amount of time is required," he explained. Savy also said that most people overestimate what they can do in one year and underestimate what they can do in ten years. Perhaps it would take us another year or two, or three, or even ten years to purchase our dream home, but I was absolutely determined to hold on tight to my dream.

Working 9 to 5 every day was not going to bring in massive amounts of money to purchase a home. Eddie was on a fixed income as well, even though he was being groomed to take over his father's business one day. Eddie's father was relatively young and had no desire to retire or hand over the business any time soon. I started to contemplate other ways to generate money, and then it dawned on me—my book!

It was time to sever the arrangement with Timothy, my agent, and self-publish my book and bring it out to the world. I was going to take matters into my own hands.

The contract I entered into with Timothy could be canceled at any time, by either party, with a thirty-day notice. My thirty-day notice letter was written and sent to Timothy in the mail. Upon receipt, he called me and apologized for not being able to secure a publisher. He wished me the best, and I did the same, and we hung up the phone.

Chapter 15

Self-publishing certainly seemed like a viable approach for an author to get their book out to the world, but it was somewhat of an expensive endeavor. I found myself digging into our savings account to cover the costs of book cover design, editing, interior layout, production, and distribution. Eddie was fully supportive, and I felt grateful.

All of the work to promote my book was being done in my spare time: evenings, lunch breaks, and weekends.

Once the book was ready to be released to the world, I had already prepared a solid media strategy and was ready to execute.

My plan was to launch the book, follow my strategy, and then reach out to literary agents and publishers within days of launching, and sell the rights to my book while there was a lot of buzz around the book. I had already secured several media venues to highlight the book. Everything was in place, ready to launch. Since most of the media publicity was scheduled to appear in the following two months, that would be the most critical time to secure an agent and a publisher.

There were several days that I was working twenty hours a day and sleeping four. Oddly enough, I felt fine. I may have been running on pure adrenaline.

One evening, around 1:30 a.m., I woke up and sat bolt upright in bed. I heard a message. The message sounded like a whisper, but it was clearly audible. The message said, *Go to the house.* That was it—no other words, other than those four.

Intuitively, I knew exactly which house the message was referring to. I decided not to tell anyone about the message as I thought others might have thought I was crazy. After work, the next day, I drove over to the lottery home, and as I approached, I observed a sign on the front lawn. It was a sign for me. It said: FOR SALE!

My heart skipped a beat. The dream home, the home I visualized me and Eddie living in and owning, was for sale. I wrote down the name and telephone number of the real estate agent, and I drove back home.

When Eddie returned from work, I told him about the message and the sign. I told Eddie that I planned to call the agent and schedule a visit. His logical mind kicked in, and he asked, "Okay, my love, but where is the money going to come from?"

"Wherever it is now, honey," I said with conviction and then explained further. "Savy shared a story with me about a man from India named Maharishi Mahesh Yogi who wanted to start an entire worldwide practice of transcendental meditation, and the plan involved a considerable amount of investment to get it off the ground. One of his team members asked the Maharishi where he was going to get the money to bring this to the world, and his response was from 'wherever it is now.'"

Savy shared lots of wisdom around money and abundance with me, and I found his thinking was definitely not the norm.

I went on. "Honey, I know this may seem crazy, but there is something about that home that is calling me. I feel we can own it. I don't know how, but I absolutely believe we can do it if we commit to it. Let's start by going to visit it, and we will take it from there. Would you be willing to go and visit it with me?"

Eddie replied, in the most loving way, "I understand your desire to own that home. I know you are in love with that home, but you have been in that home dozens of times, and you know that house inside and out. Besides, we spent most of our savings on the book and the book launch. We don't have the money to buy that house right now."

He had a very valid point, but I also learned from Savy that success sometimes involves violating logic. Violating logic means that you don't always do what is conventional. Sometimes, what's to be done is to listen to your heart and press the mute button on your left brain.

Reluctantly, Eddie agreed to visit the home, and my hand reached for the telephone as fast as humanly possible. I scheduled a visit the following evening.

Sleeping had become a challenge for me when I became overly excited. That night I tossed and turned all evening. We were visiting our dream home at 7 p.m., and the hours couldn't fly by fast enough.

A few minutes before 7 p.m., Eddie and I were parked in the familiar driveway awaiting the arrival of the real estate agent. Right on time, he arrived carrying the listing sheet with all of the details of this home.

As we approached the front door together, I was in full-blown visualization mode. I imagined we were coming home from work and going into our home, our front door. So, even though the agent was with us, I imagined he was visiting us at our new home.

He put the key in the lock, turned it, and we were inside. The house looked exactly as it did during the draw. Everything was still inside, from the furniture, window coverings, décor, televisions, art on the walls, bedding, towels, silk plants, and beautiful vases.

I asked the real estate agent why the winner was selling the home, and he said that she only wanted the money. This house was too big for her. She wanted to sell the home as-is, and the sale price included all of the contents.

Even though I was walking around the home cool as a cucumber, I was bursting with excitement inside, and Eddie knew it. I think my eagerness scared him to some degree because he knew that look of determination. The visit didn't take that long, as I was very familiar with this home. I wanted to view it as a buyer this time to get the feel for it. It felt really good. It felt right, and it felt like it was ours.

We thanked the agent, and said, "We'll be in touch," and headed back to our duplex. Eddie knew I wanted that house. I believe, to some degree, he felt helpless as he would have loved to buy it for me, but he didn't have the means at that time.

When I returned home, since it wasn't very late, I decided to call Savy. Savy answered immediately. I asked him if he would meet me on our usual park bench the following morning before work, and he agreed.

At our usual time, I was seated on the park bench awaiting Savy's arrival. When Savy arrived, I jumped right in. I was speaking so quickly my words were coming out like a jumble. Savy asked me to slow down and to breathe.

"Okay, Savy, I am relaxed now. Here's the thing. You know how in love I am with that dream home, right?"

"Yes, Sophie. Anyone who knows you is fully aware of your love for that dream lottery home," he said with a smile on his face.

"Well, it is for sale, and I want to buy it." There the words were out—no need for sugar-coating it. That was the fact. The home was for sale, and I wanted to buy it.

"If you want the house, get the house, Sophie. You are the only one standing in your way," Savy declared.

"Oh yeah, easy for you to say." As the words came out of my mouth, they felt a bit insulting, and I certainly didn't mean to say it sarcastically. "I'm sorry, Savy. I didn't mean to say it that way. We simply don't have the money to buy that house right now. I took all of our savings and put it into the launch of my book, and now we don't have anything to use for a deposit."

Savy quickly responded in his usual mind-blowing way. "Sophie, you don't need the money until you decide to buy the house."

Okay, now I was confused. "I don't need the money?! Of course, I need the money. You can't buy houses with stones," I said with a chuckle.

"You don't need the money until you buy the house. Once your name goes on a legally binding contract, then and only then do you need the money," Savy responded.

"But this house is expensive. It is much more than we can afford. I am not even sure we could make mortgage payments on that home." As I said these words, my volume dropped as my energy starting to become lower and lower.

"Listen, Sophie. It is neither expensive nor inexpensive; only thinking makes it so. And, who said you have to have a mortgage? If you want to own the home outright, focus on owning it outright. You are assuming you have to have a mortgage. You are thinking the way most people think. To manifest something like this, you have to think differently. You have to think about the possibility and have unwavering faith. You must know that the house is already yours and allow the Universe to find the way. Remember what I taught you about not needing to know the HOW.

"Also, the same amount of energy to manifest a small amount of money is required to manifest a large amount of money. No more effort is required. By now, you understand the manifestation process, as we have talked about it on a number of occasions. Knowing and doing are two different things. You understand this, and now you have the opportunity to implement it. This is where the *doing* comes in. Does that make sense?"

After a very brief moment of silence as I processed what Savy had just said, I exclaimed, "Oh my goodness, Savy. This is brilliant. I get it! I totally get it. Thank you. An idea just popped in my mind as you were sharing that, and I'm going to talk with Eddie. We'll call the agent today to put an offer together."

My enthusiasm was suddenly back in full form. I was going to buy this house, one way or another.

Chapter 16

The real estate agent said he would be happy to meet us at the dream home to draft up the offer.

Prior to meeting the agent, I shared the idea for the offer with Eddie. He felt my idea was completely unconventional, but he agreed that if the seller was going to accept it, he would be fully on board.

Again, we were back inside the dream home, seated comfortably at the dining room table. For a moment, I sat there thinking about our next Thanksgiving dinner, and as I glanced around the room, I saw it filled with our family. I could almost smell the turkey roasting in the oven.

The visualizations were vivid for me. I felt the reality of owning this home with all of my senses. This was our home, and I knew once our signatures were on the contract, we would find a way.

The offer was as follows: we were going to pay the seller full price, and the money would be paid in increments. We would pay 10 percent of the purchase price to the seller on the day we move in, a monthly occupancy fee for six months after that, and the balance of the sale price on closing, six months from move-in.

There were no other conditions on our offer. It was an unusual offer, yet it was a clean offer. The real estate agent felt confident we had ourselves a deal and promised to call us the moment he had news.

When we returned home, Eddie had a valid question for me. He wanted to know where the ten percent was going to come from. We hadn't discussed where the money would come from; we were both operating on blind faith. Frankly, I was surprised Eddie was even onboard—most people would think we were out of our minds.

When I was fourteen years of age, I started a retirement fund. I set it up with automatic withdrawals from my bank account to go directly into this fund. When withdrawals are taken from retirement funds prior to maturity, the government withholds the taxes. After taxes were paid, I estimated we had the exact amount of money we needed to move into the home. A friend had once explained to me that retirement is an investment, and this home was an investment, too. So, it felt like the right thing to do.

Eddie was aware of my retirement fund, but he had forgotten about it. After I explained the option of cashing in these funds, he agreed that it could work.

The rent we were paying at the duplex was exactly the same as the occupancy fee we offered. The amount we had to figure out would be the balance due within six months of moving in. By most people's standards, that was no small amount, but the way I saw it, it was already done in my imagination. Still, I am convinced most people would have thought we had lost our minds. So, we decided not to tell our parents about how we constructed the deal as they would definitely not have been supportive.

However, we did tell our landlords because we wanted to see if they were open to us breaking the lease. Fortunately, they had decided to renovate their home and were happy at the idea of us moving out earlier than planned. That was a relief. This was another sign that we were on the right track.

Two hours after we returned home, our real estate agent called to tell us we had a deal! An overwhelming sense of fear arose within me. I started to think I had gone too far in chasing my dream. In the moment of the fear arising and the negative and destructive thoughts that followed the emotion, I realized that I had an opportunity to turn that fear into faith.

Fear and faith were on the same emotional scale. Fear was simply focusing on what I didn't want. However, when I focused on the outcome that I desired, which was owning the home and imagining we owned it, the fear turned into faith.

I also reflected back to more "Savy wisdom." During a conversation about goals, Savy said the following: "Sophie, goals are not for what you get. Goals are designed to stretch you. The biggest benefit of a stretch goal is who you become along the process of pursuing the goal."

Thinking positive thoughts calmed me. I made a decision to discipline myself every single day by focusing only on what I desired and steering away from thoughts that would contaminate my goal.

Another reflection brought me to another piece of "Savy wisdom" when he said, "It only takes a little bit of poison to kill." Savy was talking about negative thinking and negative feelings. They are destructive and should be avoided at all costs.

Within weeks we were moving into our new home. Since the home was fully furnished, we sold off or gave away our furniture, which wasn't much, and got settled in.

The day we took possession of this home was an interesting one. Our move involved our personal items, dishes, pots, pans, and utensils. I could see the curious looks on our parents' faces as they walked into our new home and were taken aback by how gorgeous it was. Not one of them asked us how we could afford this home, and we didn't offer any information on that subject, either. I suppose they respected that we were adults and making our own decisions.

Eddie and I became extremely frugal with our spending. We cautiously spent and aggressively saved. After a couple of months of being in our new home, we had managed to save up some money, but it was a small fraction of what we needed. I constantly had to reassure Eddie that it was going to work out magnificently, even though there were times that I felt all consumed in fear.

When fear consumed me, I switched to faith. If fear came in multiple times a day, I switched to faith. I became really good at switching out of the negative into the positive within an instant. It was like exercising a muscle with a weight training routine.

It was now book launch time, and I took a few days off to focus on the launch of my book, to do more media interviews, and to get the queries sent out. I mailed out queries to numerous literary agents and sent the manuscript to a couple of publishers as well. I decided it was worth a try to go directly to a publisher and see how or if they respond. I had nothing to lose and lots potentially to gain.

Amazingly, within a few days, I received a dozen responses, and they all wanted to see my proposal, except for one. One publisher wanted to buy the rights to the book immediately. They felt strongly this book was going to be a mega-hit best-seller. They offered an advance of $10,000 if I signed the contract immediately. I decided to wait to see what other responses would come in.

Printing out and sending a dozen proposals was a rather big ordeal. I had to rely on the printing services of a local office supply business. My sister Brandy got involved and helped me package everything up and send it out via courier. It was also a rather large expense, but that didn't concern me as I felt strongly there would be a positive return.

One week later, I received a letter from a representative of the largest literary agency in the world. The agency, based out of New York City, was called Borealis Literary Agency. The agent's name was Colleen McCaffrey. She included a contract for me to sign along with a covering letter. Colleen suggested I sign the contract, and she would set up a bidding war. She included her telephone number and a request for me to call her once I received her package. It was evening, and I decided to wait until my lunch break the next day to call her.

12:05 p.m. the next day, I made the call to Colleen. I was a bit hesitant as I felt a sense of caution. I wondered if her offer was real and sincere. After going through the receptionist, she put me through to Colleen.

Colleen was in love with my book proposal. She told me that it was the most complete book proposal she had ever received, and additionally, she absolutely loved my manuscript and the book idea. She was ready to create an auction for publishers to bid on my book. I was surprised by this, as I had heard about auctions but never entertained implementing the auction concept for my book. Upon reflection, it made perfect sense for my book to be put up for auction, as it was already a classic in my mind.

Excitedly, I signed Colleen's contract and sent it directly back to her. She got on with her magical work.

Ten days later, my phone rang, and it was Colleen.

She said, "Sophie, are you sitting down?"

"I'm not, but I can if you want. What's up?" I asked.

"This morning, the biggest publisher in the world, Terragon Publishing, pre-empted all other bids and bought the rights to your book for $2.4 million dollars! And, a publisher in Germany bought the German rights for another $75,000."

She spoke so quickly I could hardly believe my ears.

"Oh my gosh! Seriously? This is amazing. I can hardly believe it!" I screeched.

"It is for real, Sophie. It is very real. Congratulations. I'll send you the details for their contracts as soon as they get it together, but I wanted to give you the news as soon as possible."

I hung up the phone and cried tears of joy.

Part III

Chapter 17

After I received the call from Colleen about the publishing deal and the advance, Eddie and I headed over to my parents' home to share the great news.

As we were standing in my parents' living room, the television was on in the background. When my parents were home, the television was often turned on. They loved their game shows, variety shows, sitcoms, and the evening news. While we were standing there, the news channel was on.

All of a sudden, I heard a familiar voice. I turned around only to discover Savy on the television. Below his image, a ticker tape was flowing across the screen that read, "STEPHEN ALEXANDER VAUGHAN, BILLIONAIRE."

I shrieked, "Savy! That's Savy! What is he doing on television? And, he's a billionaire? Is he the one who lives in that castle around the lake?"

Mom jumped in and suggested with a smile, "Soph, if you stop talking, we may be able to hear why he's on the news."

Nancy Hoffman, one of our most admired local news anchors, reported:

Stephen Alexander Vaughan, also known to his family and friends as Savy, has been named Man of The Year by the world's most prestigious Ginger Elite Magazine. He earned this accomplishment because of his generous contributions to the world, including his recent donation of over $100 million dollars to add a new wing at Bridlewood Children's Hospital. He's also admired by many around the world because of the constant growth of his business, which he built from the ground up. Mr. Vaughn has come a long way from his early years of being homeless and suicidal. His latest acquisition, Terragon Publishing, is the largest publishing house in the world, and his vision is to support authors who have a goal of changing the world with their books.

"Oh, my goodness. Savy acquired the publishing house that bought the rights to my book! What are the odds of that?" I shouted with surprise in my voice. I also had head-to-toe goosebumps after hearing Nancy speak and learning that Savy's origins came from an even darker place than mine.

Suddenly, I felt compelled to share my darkest secret. I turned to my parents to speak.

"Mom, Dad, do you remember years ago when I was distraught because my high school sweetheart Chad ended our relationship?"

"Yes, we sure do, honey. You were a big ole mess. We were actually quite concerned for you at that time," Mom said with a loving voice.

"Well, I had decided to end my life, and I went to the park in town to contemplate how I would do it. In the midst of an emotional breakdown, I discovered a man sitting directly beside me on the park bench. I didn't hear him arrive. I had no idea how he even got there, but 'poof' there he was. It was Savy! He literally saved my life. He gave me that handkerchief that I carry around with me. You know the one, the one that has the embroidery that says *if you want your life to change, you must change*. That is when my friendship started with Savy, and we have been meeting, and he has been guiding me with his 'Savy wisdom' ever since."

Both my parents looked at me with surprise on their faces. I wasn't sure what they were thinking, but they looked shell-shocked to some degree. Eddie was familiar with all of this, so he wasn't surprised with what I had shared, but he was surprised to see Savy on television and to discover who he really is. And I think he was surprised that I'd finally shared my dark experience with my parents.

"Mom, Dad, there's more," I continued. "There is another interesting thing about Savy that I didn't tell you. Remember the letter I received from Savy immediately following Braden's death? Savy told me that he recently had surgery and canceled our appointment for the first of January. I found out that the surgery was for a heart transplant. It wasn't until quite some time after, I realized that the timing was conspicuous, so I asked Savy when he received his heart transplant, and he told me his surgery was on December nineteenth."

I stopped talking and noticed my parent's mouths hanging open in disbelief. My mom backed up a few steps and gently sat down. I think this news really shocked them. I wasn't sure if they were happy, stunned, sad, or what they were feeling and decided to give them a few moments to assimilate this information.

Mom started first. "Hearing this, I needed to sit down. This is a lot to take in. Out of all of the emotions that I am feeling right now, in this moment, I feel gratitude. Braden saved Savy's life and as a result, Braden and Savy together, through Savy's generous donations, are likely saving hundreds and perhaps thousands of lives.

And, on top of that, his publishing house bought the rights to your book. Amazing. Simply amazing."

Then my mom seemed to have an epiphany. "When they took Braden's organs, the hospital staff asked us if we wanted to know who received his organs. They said that they couldn't tell us the name, but they could offer us some information on the recipient, including age and gender. We told them we wanted to know. They donated Braden's corneas from his eyes, his liver, both kidneys, and his heart and lungs. We heard Braden's donation saved a baby, who received the liver. A teenage girl received one of the kidneys, a mom of three received the other kidney, and a man in his early twenties received his lungs. The corneas, we have no idea. The hospital said that the information for the heart transplant was unavailable and private, and the recipient had asked to keep it that way."

Dad jumped in. "Sophie, if you could arrange for us to meet Savy, we would really love that."

"I believe I can arrange that dad, in fact, I'd love for you to meet him," I said with confidence.

I felt so much pride for Savy. I already knew he was an incredible man, and it was wonderful to see him being acknowledged in this way, being honored as the Man of the Year. He deeply deserved it.

Minutes later, Eddie headed into the kitchen to get the champagne he put on ice. We brought champagne with us to celebrate the book deal. Dad grabbed the champagne flutes, and we poured the champagne and toasted Savy's accomplishments, as well as my accomplishment. I had never felt more grateful in my life.

I felt gratitude for my mom and dad, my whole family, and my husband Eddie. I was grateful for Savy. I was grateful to secure the publishing contract for my book. I felt gratitude for every area of my life, and I knew that life was about to get even better and better every day in every way.

The following day, this letter arrived in the mail, addressed to me from Savy:

My Dear Sophie,

I am writing this note to you with a very happy heart. Knowing you, Eddie and your family are in such a beautiful space, enjoying so much of life's goodness is something I have always longed to see.

Sophie, we both know I was guided to the park bench on that misty morning oh so many years ago. Sitting beside you, Sophie, I could feel your energy, your sadness. It was breaking my heart. I wanted to reach out and hold you in my arms and just tell you it's okay, but I was certain I would scare you. And, I knew I was guided there to help you. Your soul was crying out to God at that time. I prayed that day that you would accept my offer of help.

We now know you had a choice, and unfortunately, so many individuals who are in the mental state you were in that day reject the assistance they are screaming for. They are not ready, Sophie.

You are such a beautiful, courageous soul. You have followed through on every lesson that I have taught you. You are now able to guide others as I have guided you. We both know that all people are equal. We are God's highest form of creation; the only difference exists in awareness. And that awareness is what creates the obvious differences.

People are naturally drawn to you, Sophie, because of your energy. They feel your goodness and your willingness to provide service. You have become one of the most service-oriented individuals I have had the pleasure of knowing. I particularly love the way you leave everyone you meet with the impression of increase. Continue to share these lessons in your writing and in your everyday behavior.

Time changes everything, Sophie. We both have very busy lives today and may not have the opportunity to visit as often as we have in the past. However, I want you to know that as long as my heart continues to beat, we will be connected, my dear friend.

Go forth and share your awareness with others. Sophie, the success you are enjoying is merely one small step in the direction of greater things you will do, many of which are beyond your wildest dreams.

Your loving friend.

In spirit,

P.S.: I must mention Sophie, although I am sure you are already aware of this truth. Every time I have been with you over these years, every time, I forget to bring this to your attention. I have neglected to tell you that Chad's leaving was no accident. Chad had to leave to create a space for the good that your heart desired.

The End

About The Author

Peggy McColl is a world-renowned wealth, business and manifestation expert as well as the New York Times Best Selling Author of *Your Destiny Switch: Master Your Key Emotions And Attract the Life of Your Dreams.*

For over 26+ years at the time of this publication, using her Power Life Script® process — along with her unique intimate understanding of the Universal Laws - she has been showing people from around the globe how to:

**Manifest any result they desire
in their personal and professional lives,
from dream homes and soulmates
to perfect health and multi-million-dollar
businesses;**

Become International Best-Selling Authors;

Create wealth and complete freedom;

And much more.

She has worked with – and been endorsed by – some of the most renowned experts in the personal development field including…

Bob Proctor
Neale Donald Walsch
Jim Rohn
Dr. Wayne Dyer
Mark Victor Hansen
Caroline Myss
Gregg Braden
Debbie Ford
Arielle Ford
Hay House
Marianne Williamson
Dean Graziosi
Gay Hendricks
Marie Forleo
And many others

Peggy's special, unique & intensive programs, speaking engagements, goal achievement seminars, and best-selling books have inspired & instructed "everyday" individuals, entrepreneurs, authors and organizations to reach their maximum potential and truly take massive quantum leaps.

Peggy can help you to realize your success (both mentally, spiritually, and in "the real world"), whatever your chosen field may be! Whether you want to manifest a dream life, build your business, publish your book, or make money online, Peggy has the proven track record to help you achieve your goals.

To explore the ways in which Peggy can help you demand more of yourself and live your dreams, please visit:

{ www.PeggyMcColl.com }

For step-by-step guidance on creating your dream life using your own Power Life Script®, visit:

{ www.PowerLifeScript.com }

Made in the USA
Columbia, SC
08 January 2021

30506618R00104